Published by IPC Magazines Ltd., King's Reach Tower, Stamford Street, London SE1 9LS. Sole agents for Australia and New Zealand: Gordon & Gotch Ltd. South Africa: Central News Agency. Reproduction by New Era Graphics, London. Printed and bound by Vlasveld B.V., Rotterdam, Holland.

ISB Number 85037 717-X

All football facts correct at time of going to press

ROY OF THE ROVERS

IT WAS THE LAST KICK OF THE MATCH...
CONGRATULATIONS, TONY! OLDFIELD WILL STAY UP IF YOU KEEP PLAYING LIKE YOU DID TODAY!
THANK YOU, ROY... WE WERE LUCKY TO CATCH YOU ON AN OFF DAY!
HIGHEST
GOOD GRIEF! LOOK AT THE STATE OF YOU LOT!
OOOH! DON'T SHOUT, BOYS...I'M EXHAUSTED!
I DON'T MIND IF YOU DROP ME FOR NEXT WEEK'S GAME... I NEED A REST!
THAT SETTLES IT! YOU'RE ALL GOING TO TAKE A WEEK'S HOLIDAY IN THE SUN! WE'LL GET RIGHT AWAY FROM FOOTBALL!
GREAT!
SMASHING!
FANTASTIC!
HOW DID YOU ORGANISE THIS AT SUCH SHORT NOTICE, ROY? IT'S INCREDIBLE!
YOU JUST HAVE TO TALK TO THE RIGHT PEOPLE, CARL! NOW WHERE'S NOEL BAXTER GOT TO? HE'S LATE!
HERE HE COMES!
AIRWAYS
FLY
OCH! THE MAN'S AN IDIOT!
KEEP YOUR COMMENTS TO YOURSELF, McKAY... AT LEAST I'M GETTING INTO THE SPIRIT OF THINGS!
SOON, THEY WERE AIRBORNE...
NOW WE CAN RELAX... AND FORGET ALL ABOUT FOOTBALL!

SEVERAL HOURS LATER, THEY ARRIVED ON THE HOLIDAY ISLAND... AND IT WAS RAINING!
WELCOME TO SUNNY MAJORCA
HOW ARE YOU DOING, NOEL? YOU LOOK NICE AND DRY!
IF YOU SAY ONE MORE WORD, YOU'RE GOING TO FIND YOURSELF ON THE INJURY LIST, MCKAY!
SOON...
SENOR RACE? I AM DIEGO... I WILL TRANSPORT YOU TO YOUR HOTEL JOLLY QUICK!
MARIA
WELCOM MELCHESTA ROWVAS F.C.
IF THE COACH LOOKS LIKE THAT, JUST IMAGINE WHAT THE HOTEL WILL BE LIKE!
THERE THEY ARE!
MELCHESTER ROVERS!
I THINK WE'VE PLAYED THIS SCENE BEFORE... LET'S GET OUT OF HERE!
VIVA MELCHESTER!
BUT...
HUMBLE APOLOGIES, SENOR! THE ENGINE, IT WILL NOT START... IT IS THE RAIN!
WELL, THERE'S NO POINT IN STAYING IN HERE... WE MIGHT AS WELL GO OUTSIDE AND SIGN A FEW AUTOGRAPHS!
WHAT A HOLIDAY! OUR COACH HAS BROKEN DOWN, I'M SOAKED TO THE SKIN, AND I THINK I'M STARTING TO GET WRITER'S CRAMP!
IF YOU BORED WITH WRITING, SENOR- WE PLAY A LITTLE FOOTBALL TO PASS THE TIME. YES?
AND SO...
GOAAAAAAAL!
EL ROCKETO! FANTASTIC GOAL, SENOR RACE!
THE "MATCH" WAS FULL OF ACTION...
OVER TO YOU, NOEL!
BEAUTIFUL PASS, BOSS!

AAAARGH!
APOLOGIES, AMIGO... AN ACCIDENT!
HA-HAAA! POOR OLD NOEL!
IT'S NOT FUNNY... I'M SOAKED AGAIN! AND ANY-WAY, I THOUGHT WE WERE MEANT TO BE GETTING AWAY FROM FOOTBALL!
THEN...
SENOR RACE! I HAVE FIXED THE COACH AT LAST... WE CAN NOW LEAVE FOR YOUR HOTEL!
MAJO
THIS IS WHERE OUR HOLIDAY REALLY STARTS! NO MORE SOCCER!
AFTER A FEW MILES...
DIEGO! YOUR ENGINE'S SMOKING!
FEAR NOT, AMIGO! THE HOTEL... SHE IS CLOSE!
IT'LL JUST BE A PILE OF BRICKS AND MORTAR ON A BUILDING SITE, I BET!
BUT...
INCREDIBLE!
WOW! WHAT A PAD!
WE CERTAINLY WEREN'T EXPECTING THIS!
WELCOME TO HOTEL PARADISE, SENOR RACE... I HOPE YOU WILL ENJOY YOUR STAY!
SO DO I!
DON'T USE THE REVOLVING DOORS, DUNCAN– THOSE THINGS CAN BE DANGEROUS!
RUBBISH! THEY'RE AS SAFE AS HOUSES!

BUT...
HELP! THE DOORS ARE JAMMED!
TOLD YOU SO!
HUMBLE APOLOGIES! THE HOTEL IS NEW... WE HAVEN'T TESTED EVERYTHING YET!
GOOD GRIEF!
AFTER DUNCAN HAD BEEN FREED...
WELL, THIS LOOKS VERY NICE!
IT SHOULD BE AT THE PRICE! I'M GOING TO HAVE A SHOWER TO COOL OFF AFTER THAT TERRIBLE JOURNEY!
MINUTES LATER...
YOWWWWW!
ROY! WHAT'S WRONG?
THE COLD WATER'S BOILING HOT!
HOW ABOUT THE HOT WATER?
IT'S FREEZING COLD!
WHAT A PLACE! I WONDER IF ALL THE OTHER ROOMS ARE THE SAME?
OUTSIDE IN THE CORRIDOR...
THE BATHROOM DOOR'S STUCK... CHARLIE CARTER CAN'T GET OUT!
OUR FLOOR'S FLOODED... IT'S LIKE A SWAMP IN THERE!
IT'S ALL RIGHT FOR YOU LOT... WE HAVEN'T EVEN MANAGED TO OPEN OUR DOOR YET!
SOMEONE CALL THE MANAGER!
BUT YOU ARE THE MANAGER, ROY!
VERY FUNNY! I MEANT THE HOTEL MANAGER!

HOURS LATER...
THAT'S EVERYTHING SORTED OUT AT LAST! WHAT ARE WE GOING TO DO TONIGHT, ROY?
AS LONG AS WE FORGET ABOUT FOOTBALL, I DON'T MIND WHAT WE DO! THERE'S A FILM SHOW ON IN THE CINEMA... WE MIGHT AS WELL GO ALONG AND BE ENTERTAINED!
THE HOTEL PARADISE PRESENTS
IT COULD BE 'RAIDERS OF THE LOST ARK'!
NO, I THINK IT'LL BE 'JAWS'!
YOU'RE BOTH WRONG... IT'S GOING TO BE 'STAR WARS'!
N-NO! I DON'T BELIEVE IT!
FOOTBALL AGAIN!
STAR SOCCER
FROM THE START, MELCHESTER WERE ON THE ATTACK AND PORTFIELD FOUND THEMSELVES UNDER HEAVY PRESSURE! IN THE SECOND HALF IT STARTED TO RAIN!
DO YOU REMEMBER WHAT HAPPENED NEXT, ROY?
YES, BUT I'D RATHER FORGET ABOUT IT, BLACKIE!
SAAAAVVVVED!
JOHNSON'S TIPPED IT ON TO HIS CROSSBAR, BUT CAN RACEY PUT THE REBOUND INTO THE NET?
YESSSSS! FANTASTIC HEADER, ROY!
THAT WAS A CLEAN GOAL ALL THE WAY!
WHY DID YOU HAVE TO SAY CLEAN FOR, NOEL?

LOOK AT THE STATE OF ME!

STILL TRYING TO FORGET ABOUT FOOTBALL, THE ROVERS SPENT THE NEXT DAY SUNBATHING...
THIS IS THE LIFE!
YOU CAN'T BEAT RELAXING IN THE SUN!
I WONDER HOW MUCH OF A TAN WE CAN GET IN SIX DAYS?

SUDDENLY...
WHAT THE-?
EUUUUCH!
YOWWW!
ER... MAY WE HAVE OUR BALL BACK, SENORS?
WE ARE A LOCAL AMATEUR SIDE. THE HOTEL ALLOWS US TO PRACTISE ON THIS WASTE GROUND!
WHO ARE YOU GUYS?
WOULD THE GREAT MELCHESTER ROVERS LIKE A MATCH WITH US? WE WILL BE MOST HONOURED IF YOU DID!

WELL, I DON'T KNOW... WE'RE SUPPOSED TO BE AVOIDING FOOTBALL!
COME ON, ROY... WHY DON'T WE GIVE THEM A GAME?
WE CAN'T DISAPPOINT THE KIDS
DUNCAN AND BLACKIE ARE RIGHT, BOSS... LET'S MAKE THEIR DAY!

AND SO...
GO ON, CARL... SEE IF YOU CAN GET A QUICK GOAL!
NO PROBLEM, BOSS!

BUT...
GRACIAS, AMIGO!
CARL HUNT'S BEEN ROBBED!
GOOOOAAAAL!
I THINK THIS MATCH IS GOING TO BE HARDER THAN WE THOUGHT, ROY!
I RECKON YOU'RE RIGHT, BLACKIE... FIRST DIVISION FOOTBALL MIGHT BE EASY COMPARED TO THIS!
SIX DAYS LATER, THE ROVERS RETURNED HOME. GENERAL MANAGER BEN GALLOWAY WAS WAITING TO MEET THEM...
WELCOME BACK, BLACKIE... YOU ALL LOOK FIT AND RELAXED AFTER YOUR SHORT BREAK!
WELL, MOST OF US ARE, BEN!
WHERE'S ROY GOT TO? HAS HE BEEN HELD UP BY CUSTOMS?
NO, HERE HE COMES NOW!
ROY! DON'T TELL ME... YOU INJURED YOURSELF PLAYING FOOTBALL IN SPAIN!
WE DID PLAY A VERY HARD MATCH AGAINST SOME SPANISH LADS... IT ENDED IN A FOUR-ALL DRAW!
BUT I DIDN'T HURT MYSELF DURING THE GAME... I TWISTED MY ANKLE AS I WAS WALKING DOWN THE STEPS OF THE 'PLANE JUST NOW!
WHAT ARE YOU ALL LAUGHING AT? IT'S NOT FUNNY!
ROY WAS THE ONLY MELCHESTER PLAYER WHO WAS NOT FIT TO PLAY IN THE NEXT MATCH...
COME ON, ROVERS... WE WANT SIX!
THE HUNTER'S MADE IT FIVE!
NEXT TIME I TAKE THE TEAM ON A MID-SEASON BREAK, WE'LL GO TO BOGNOR! IT'LL BE A LOT SAFER!
The End

Norman conquers

At 17 Norman Whiteside became the youngest-ever player to appear in the World Cup Finals when he starred for Northern Ireland in Spain. At 18 he established himself in the Manchester United side! It was a case of country-before-club for the striker turned midfielder who had made only one full appearance for United before becoming a World Cup star.

Miller the marvel

Willie Miller is now in his ninth season as captain of Aberdeen and it's been success nearly all the way for the powerful defender. He's helped The Dons to success at home and in Europe, establishing himself in the Scotland team alongside club-mate Alex McLeish. Miller could have signed for an English team, but his loyalty has been rewarded with a cupboard full of trophies and international caps.

Charlie is their darling

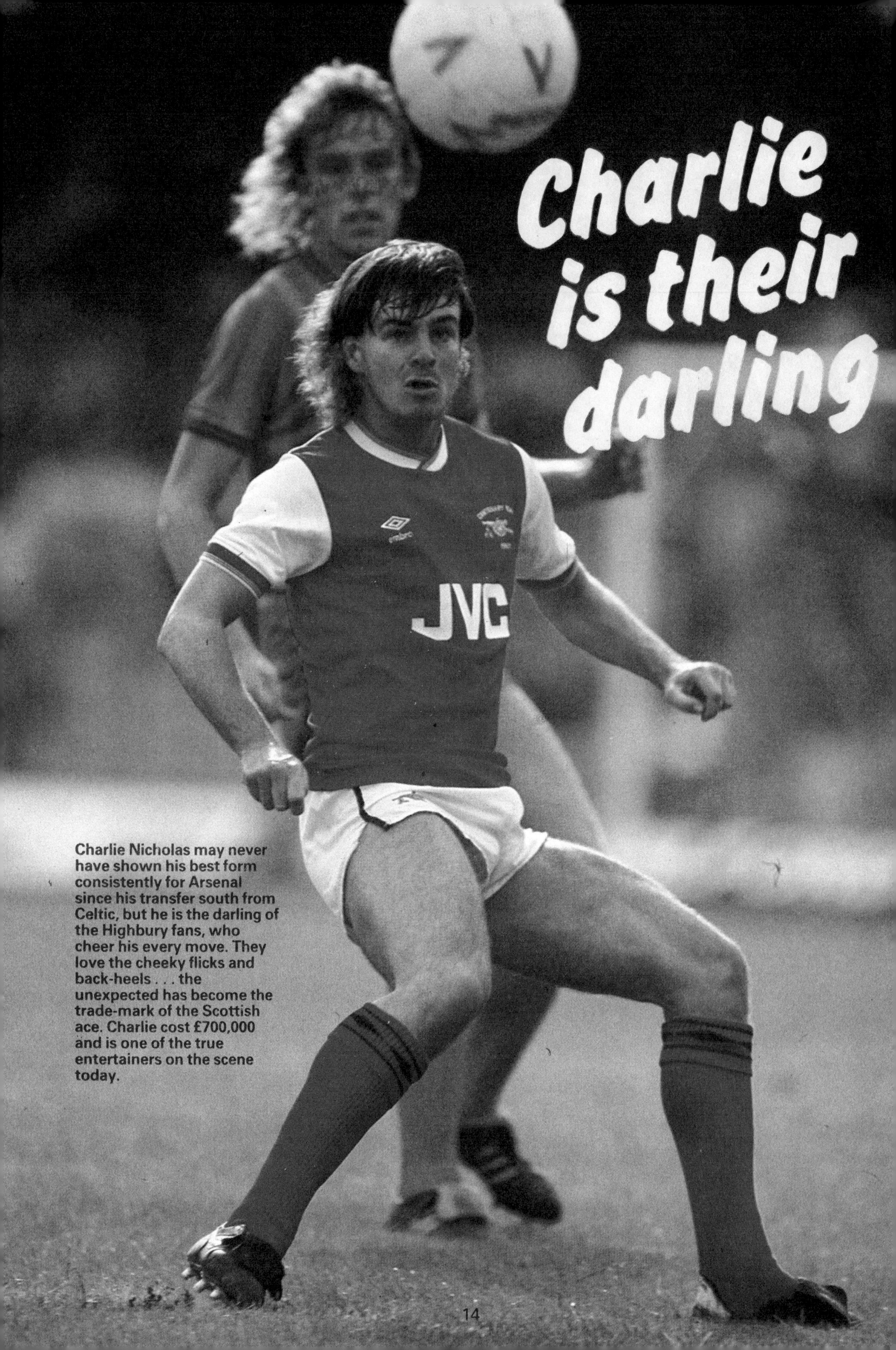

Charlie Nicholas may never have shown his best form consistently for Arsenal since his transfer south from Celtic, but he is the darling of the Highbury fans, who cheer his every move. They love the cheeky flicks and back-heels . . . the unexpected has become the trade-mark of the Scottish ace. Charlie cost £700,000 and is one of the true entertainers on the scene today.

IN A RUSH TO SCORE!

Top foreign clubs would pay millions of pounds for Liverpool striker Ian Rush. But the Welsh international is on a long-term contract at Anfield and his ambition is to help Liverpool to more honours. Rush began his career with Chester and signed for The Reds in a £300,000 deal in 1980. He was voted Young Player of the Year in 1983 and Rush now forms arguably the most lethal strike-force in world football for Wales with Manchester United's Mark Hughes. What a pity the pair didn't have the chance to display their many skills in the World Cup Finals in Mexico.

Super Simon

Simon Stainrod couldn't stop scoring after he signed for Aston Villa in 1985. Not that the Villa Park fans were complaining! Stainrod averaged a goal-a-game following his transfer from Sheffield Wednesday, where he never really settled down. Stainrod formed a dangerous partnership with Andy Gray and it was goals galore as Stainrod found the form that put him in the England reckoning as a Queen's Park Rangers player.

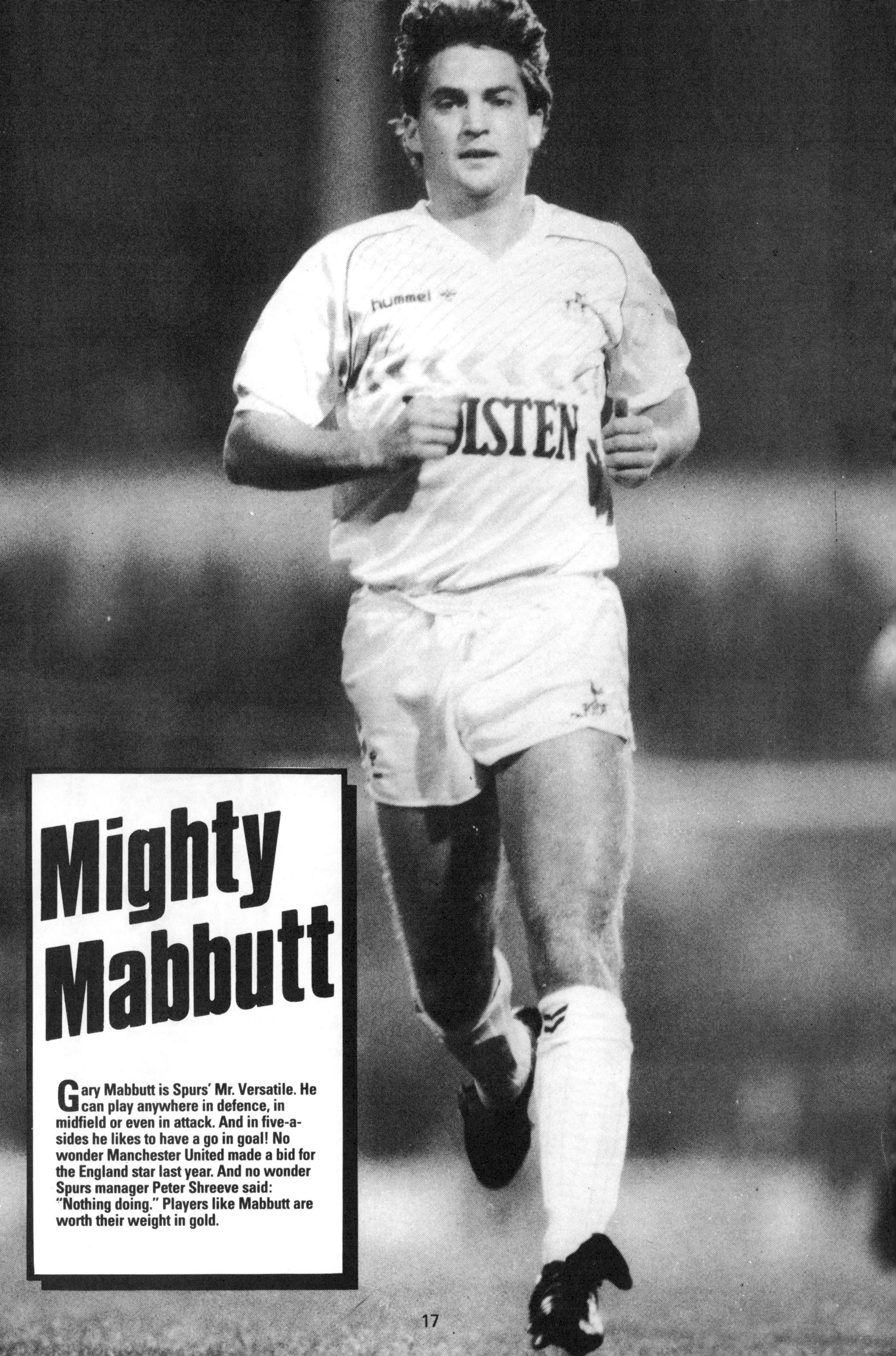

Mighty Mabbutt

Gary Mabbutt is Spurs' Mr. Versatile. He can play anywhere in defence, in midfield or even in attack. And in five-a-sides he likes to have a go in goal! No wonder Manchester United made a bid for the England star last year. And no wonder Spurs manager Peter Shreeve said: "Nothing doing." Players like Mabbutt are worth their weight in gold.

CASTLEBURN UNITED
BACK ROW ALAN REGAN · SAM YOUNG · GRAHAM MORTLAKE · BRIAN WELLS · CENTRE ROW ROGER BURTON · GORDON CHURCH ·
OLIVER DOYLE · NORMAN HAMPTON · SITTING KEITH KERR · PHIL HUGHES (CAPTAIN) · ERIC MILLS (MANAGER) · JACK CHELSEY · JOE SHAW (COACH)

JACK of UNITED

JACK CHELSEY PLAYED FOR FAMOUS CASTLEBURN UNITED, AND HIS BROTHER JIMMY FOR THEIR GREAT LOCAL RIVALS, CASTLEBURN CITY. THERE WAS ALWAYS PLENTY OF GOOD-NATURED ARGUING GOING ON IN THE CHELSEY FAMILY, ESPECIALLY WHEN BOTH CITY AND UNITED REACHED THE SEMI-FINALS OF A SPONSORED TOURNAMENT...

THEIR PARENTS JOINED IN THE DEBATE...

I'LL BACK UNITED TO BEAT MANDOVER IN THEIR SEMI-FINAL, EVEN THOUGH MANDOVER DID WIN THE FAIRS CUP!

AND I CAN'T SEE TAMHEED STANDING ANY CHANCE AGAINST CITY. THEY HOLD THE LEAGUE CUP, BUT THEY'VE HAD A POOR SEASON!

JACK CHUCKLED...

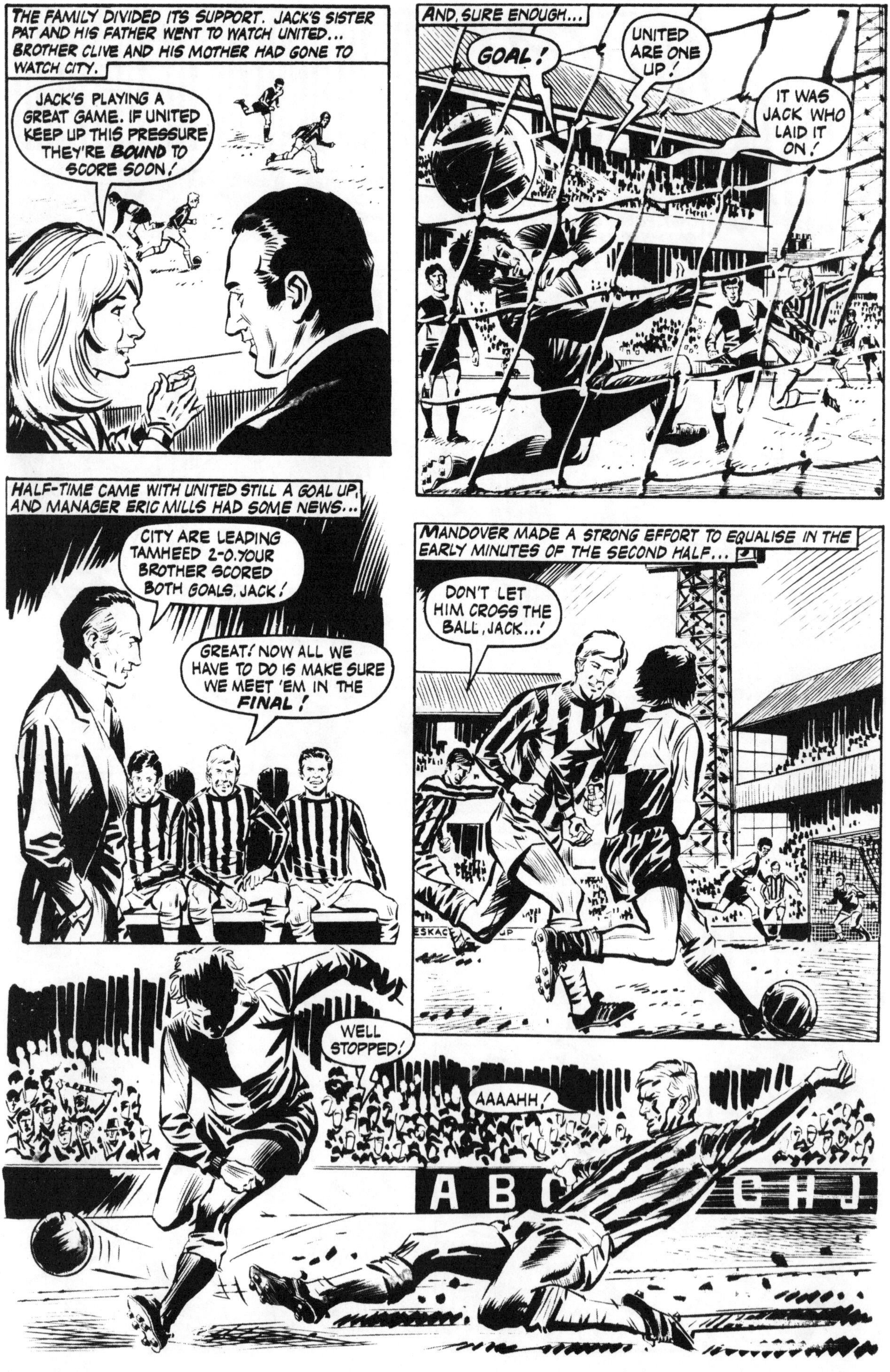

HALF-TIME CAME WITH UNITED STILL A GOAL UP, AND MANAGER ERIC MILLS HAD SOME NEWS...

CITY ARE LEADING TAMHEED 2-0. YOUR BROTHER SCORED BOTH GOALS, JACK!

GREAT! NOW ALL WE HAVE TO DO IS MAKE SURE WE MEET 'EM IN THE ***FINAL***!

MANDOVER MADE A STRONG EFFORT TO EQUALISE IN THE EARLY MINUTES OF THE SECOND HALF...

DON'T LET HIM CROSS THE BALL, JACK...!

WELL STOPPED!

AAAAHH!

UNITED SKIPPER PHIL HUGHES NOTICED THAT JACK WAS LIMPING AS HE PICKED HIMSELF UP...
YOU ALL RIGHT, JACK?
SURE... JUST A LITTLE KNOCK! NOTHING TO WORRY ABOUT.
B C
UNITED HELD FIRM, AND THE MANDOVER ATTACK FADED AWAY...
UNITED ARE ALL OVER 'EM!
WE COULD DO WITH ANOTHER GOAL TO CLINCH IT!
FRONT-RUNNER NORMAN HAMPTON RETURNED JACK'S PASS...
THIS IS UNITED'S SECOND—IT MUST BE!
IN WITH IT, JACK!
BUT JACK TOOK TIME TO CHANGE FEET...
COME ON! GET A MOVE ON!
THE DELAY GAVE A DEFENDER TIME TO CLOSE IN...
HE'S MISSED IT!
PAT WAS DISMAYED...
OUR JACK'S NOT NORMALLY AS SLOW AS THAT!
I DON'T THINK HE'S TOO HAPPY ABOUT HIS RIGHT FOOT!
UNITED MANAGED TO HOLD THEIR LEAD UNTIL THE FINAL WHISTLE...
WELL, WE WON!
WE MADE HARD WORK OF IT, THOUGH!
CITY WON 5-2. SO IT'LL BE A CRACKERJACK OF A LOCAL DERBY FOR THE FINAL!

THE TRAINER CAUGHT JACK BY THE ELBOW...
LET'S HAVE A LOOK AT THAT RIGHT ANKLE, JACK. THAT'S WHY YOU MISSED THAT SHOT, WASN'T IT?
IT'S NOTHING MUCH. A BIT SORE, THAT'S ALL.

OOOWW!
I THOUGHT SO!
DOES THIS MEAN JACK WON'T BE FIT FOR THE FINAL?

IT'S TOO EARLY TO SAY YET...
BUT I MUST PLAY! IT'LL BE THE MOST IMPORTANT GAME OF THE SEASON TO THE CHELSEY FAMILY.
THERE'S NO 'MUST' ABOUT IT! I NEVER PLAY A MAN UNLESS HE'S 100% FIT!

JIMMY WAS IN A BUBBLING MOOD WHEN JACK ARRIVED HOME...
GREAT, ISN'T IT, JACK? YOU AND ME IN THE FINAL...
YOU, YES, BUT I'M NOT SO SURE ABOUT ME! THE TRAINER'S GOT DOUBTS ABOUT MY ANKLE. I'VE GOT TO REST IT.

JACK HATED BEING INACTIVE...
HOW'S IT FEELING, JACK?
NO DIFFERENT. WHAT'S THE GOOD OF SITTING HERE WITH MY FOOT STUCK UP? I SHOULD BE DOING SOMETHING!

THE TRAINER IS THE EXPERT. HE MUST KNOW BEST.
IN THIS CASE, I'M NOT SO SURE. I JUST FEEL THAT I OUGHT TO BE EXERCISING IT TO GET IT STRONG!

A FEW DAYS LATER...
OOOUCH!
WHAT THE BLAZES DOES JACK THINK HE'S DOING OUT THERE? HE'S BEEN TOLD NOT TO TRY TO KICK A BALL!
UNITED

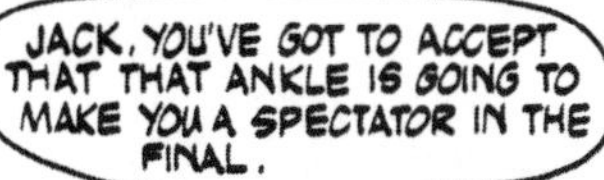
JACK, YOU'VE GOT TO ACCEPT THAT THAT ANKLE IS GOING TO MAKE YOU A SPECTATOR IN THE FINAL.

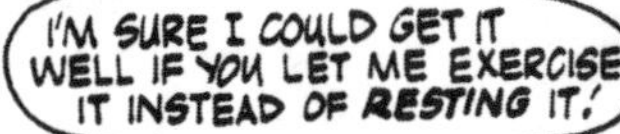
I'M SURE I COULD GET IT WELL IF YOU LET ME EXERCISE IT INSTEAD OF RESTING IT!

IT MIGHT WORK, BUT IT'S A GAMBLE I'M NOT PREPARED TO TAKE!

WHEN JACK RETURNED HOME HE GAVE HIS FATHER A SURPRISE...
WHAT HAVE YOU GOT THERE?
A SECOND-HAND BIKE. I JUST BOUGHT IT.

I'M TAKING THE LEFT-HAND PEDAL OFF.
WHAT THE HECK FOR?

THEN...
AAAAAGH!
WHAT ARE YOU TRYING TO DO- MAKE THINGS WORSE?

I CAN'T MAKE THEM WORSE! IF I FOLLOW THE TRAINER'S ADVICE I SHAN'T BE IN THE FINAL ANYWAY... SO THERE'S NO HARM IN TRYING SOMETHING MORE DRASTIC!

DON'T RIDE THAT ONE-PEDAL WRECK ON THE STREET. YOU'LL CAUSE AN ACCIDENT!
IT'S ALL RIGHT, DAD. I'M GOING TO PUSH IT DOWN TO THE PARK!

THAT EVENING, WHEN ERIC MILLS WAS EXERCISING HIS DOG IN THE PARK...
HELLO, MR. MILLS! COME TO SEE HOW JACK'S BEEN GETTING ON? HE'S BEEN RIDING THAT THING ROUND AND ROUND ALL DAY.
GOOD GRIEF! I HAD NO IDEA—!
THE FOLLOWING MORNING, AS ERIC WAS TELLING HIS TRAINER WHAT HE HAD SEEN...
JACK'S JUST DETERMINED TO GET FIT...
HOW ABOUT GIVING ME A WORK-OUT, ERIC? I FEEL FINE...
WOW! I'M GLAD I'M WEARING GLOVES!
JACK'S TREATMENT SEEMS TO HAVE WORKED!
ALL RIGHT, JACK... YOU'VE PROVED YOUR POINT! YOU CAN GO HOME AND TELL THE FAMILY YOU'RE IN FOR THE FINAL!
BUT EVEN WHEN THE BIG GAME STARTED, MILLS STILL HAD NIGGLING DOUBTS...
I'M NOT RISKING ANYTHING. IF JACK'S ANKLE SHOWS SIGNS OF BREAKING DOWN, I'M SENDING ON THE SUBSTITUTE RIGHT AWAY!
UNITED
CITY GAINED POSSESSION AND SET JIMMY ON THE MOVE...
COME ON, JIMMY!
STOP HIM, JACK!
JIMMY'S FULL OF TRICKS! I MUSTN'T TAKE MY EYE OFF THE BALL!
BUT AS JACK WENT IN, JIMMY FOXED HIM BY PULLING THE BALL BACK...
JIMMY'S A PROPER SURPRISE PACKET!
EVEN HIS OWN BROTHER CAN'T TELL WHAT HE'LL DO NEXT!

JIMMY HAD GIVEN HIMSELF SPACE TO GET ROUND JACK!
JACK'S LOST HIM! NOW UNITED ARE IN REAL TROUBLE!

THE YOUNGER CHELSEY BROTHER SET OFF ON ONE OF HIS FANTASTIC, TEASING RUNS... AND THE OUTCOME WAS NEVER IN DOUBT!
JIMMY HAS SCORED!
CITY ARE ONE UP!

ERIC MILLS SCOWLED QUESTIONINGLY...
WHAT HAPPENED? DO WE HAVE JACK OFF? DID HIS ANKLE LET HIM DOWN?
I DON'T THINK SO. HE'S RUNNING STRONGLY ENOUGH NOW.

HALF-TIME CAME AND WENT, WITH THE CITY DEFENCE STUBBORNLY THWARTING ALL UNITED'S EFFORTS TO DRAW LEVEL...
IT ISN'T UNITED'S DAY. THEY JUST CAN'T GET THE BALL IN!

THE ACCURATE BALL WAS CLEARED TO DROP IN FRONT OF JIMMY...
JIMMY'S AWAY AGAIN! IF HE CAN MAKE IT 2-0 THAT'LL CLINCH IT!
THERE'S ONLY PHIL HUGHES BETWEEN HIM AND GOAL!

JIMMY REPEATED HIS TRICK OF PULLING THE BALL BACK WHEN HE WAS CHALLENGED...
HUGHES DOESN'T KNOW HOW TO DEAL WITH JIMMY!

NOW TURN TO PAGE 99 FOR THE THRILL-PACKED CONTINUATION OF THIS GREAT STORY!

GREAT BRITAIN X1

It will almost certainly never happen. But suppose . . . just suppose . . . a Great Britain team got together. Perhaps for a worthwhile charity on the lines of Live Aid – let's call it Soccer Aid. And Great Britain had to take on the world at Wembley. It would be one of the biggest football spectaculars ever seen . . . but it would present a GREAT problem. Because there are so many GREAT players in Britain that just about every football follower would come up with a different team! You may not agree with our choice, but we think our Great Britain XI would be more than a match for the Rest of the World side.

GREAT BRITAIN XI

1 PETER SHILTON (ENGLAND)

The Rest of the World XI would want Shilts, too, but he's ours! The Southampton and England goalkeeper has emerged as one of the finest of modern times. As a youngster with Leicester, Shilton was in the original party of 40 for the 1970 World Cup Finals in Mexico. Years later he played a major role in helping England towards the 1986 Finals in that same country. He's England's most capped goalkeeper and 100 caps is not beyond his reach. He's as fit as he ever was, a perfectionist who believes he should have stopped every goal he conceded . . . and quite simply, head and shoulders above his rivals.

2 STEVE NICOL (SCOTLAND)

Steve followed the classic Liverpool tradition after his £300,000 transfer from Ayr. He was promptly put in the reserves to learn his trade. Steve has emerged as a player of valuable versatility, at home as an attacking full-back or a midfield powerhouse. Liverpool have used him as the successor to right-back Phil Neal, but he's the type of player every squad needs . . . someone who can fill in just about anywhere in case of emergency. We'll be seeing plenty of Steve on the soccer scene for years to come.

3 KENNY SANSOM (ENGLAND)

An easy choice, because over the years the Arsenal skipper has been a model of consistency. Never seems to have a bad day . . . a player who has set and maintained the highest standards. Has no rival to the England number three shirt. Even if he did, Sansom would fight off the challenge. Strong in the tackle, he is ever ready to join in the attack and is often found being marked by the opposing winger!

4 GRAEME SOUNESS (SCOTLAND)

Scotland fans have always thought Souness has been a better player for club than country. But the former Liverpool midfielder, now playing in Italy for Sampdoria, is a player admired and respected throughout the world. Not only is he a huge influence as a midfield star, his personality and leadership are vital to the team. It took Liverpool a while to recover from his departure and that is the highest praise any player could receive.

5 MARK WRIGHT (ENGLAND)

Prone to lapses of inconsistency, but generally speaking a steady centre-half who has more pace than his rivals. That is essential in the modern game, with razor sharp forwards. Wright has had his problems with Southampton, but he's come through the testing time to emerge as a truly international-class defender.

6 WILLIE MILLER (SCOTLAND)

It's been non-stop success for the Aberdeen captain over the past few years. And much of this is down to Miller's ability as a central defender and skipper. One of those players who never seems to have a bad game, Miller has come up against the best strikers in the world . . . and few have come out on top. A great defender that strikers hate!

Graeme Souness (left) would add the necessary steel to the midfield and that, coupled with his undoubted passing ability, would make him a vital asset in the Great Britain team. Glenn Hoddle and Norman Whiteside (above) could combine to unlock any defence. Hoddle with his vision, delicate touch and silky skills, and Whiteside whose power in the air and surging runs into the penalty box make him such a dangerous opponent. The goalscorers – who better than Welsh sensation Ian Rush (right).

7 BRYAN ROBSON (ENGLAND – CAPTAIN)

His £1.75m transfer from West Brom to Manchester United is likely to remain a British record for a long, long time. And the England powerhouse is the natural captain for our Great Britain XI. He goes in where it hurts . . . where the boots are flying . . . and that's why he's had his share of knocks. But there isn't a more complete midfield player in the country.

8 NORMAN WHITESIDE (N. IRELAND)

One day, Robson's United team-mate may have the sort of all-round skills his skipper has. Because since moving back from attack to midfield, Whiteside has become twice the player. And he was a pretty good striker! His tackles bite and with two World Cup campaigns behind him already, the Irish youngster (yes, he's still young!) has everything to look forward to.

9 IAN RUSH (WALES)

Liverpool tied him to a long-term contract, which is their gain and the top European clubs' loss. Rush is Mr. Goals, a player who can create a goal out of nothing. Give him even a quarter chance . . . and chances are he'll score. He makes goalscoring seem easy – but in fact it's the hardest job in football. Although he went through an unusual lean spell during the 1985/6 season he quickly got back to normal!

10 GLENN HODDLE (ENGLAND)

At first there were doubts: could Hoddle do the business at international level? In 1985 Bobby Robson finally gave the Spurs ace the extended run he'd been wanting – and Hoddle erased the doubts with a string of superb performances. He's added steel to his skills and is now a player who can both tackle and create. On an exceptionally good day, he has the fans drooling!

11 GARY LINEKER (ENGLAND)

We chose Gary to form a Magnificent Merseyside partnership with Ian Rush in attack. With Leicester he was a prolific scorer. And he proved that he could do it for England following his move to Everton last year. Scored some vital World Cup goals and is dangerous both in the air and on the ground.

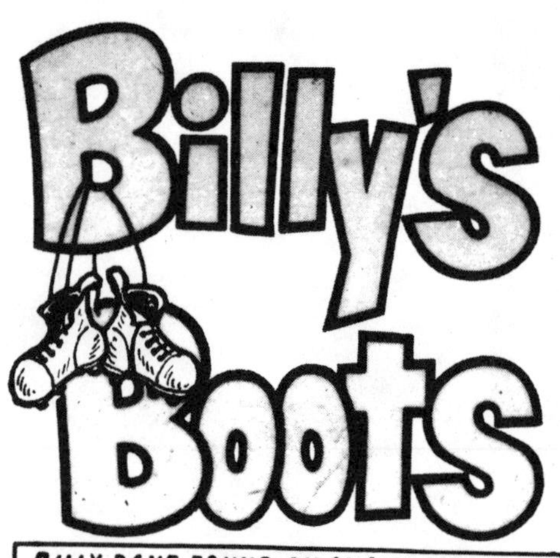

BILLY DANE FOUND AN ANCIENT PAIR OF FOOTBALL BOOTS THAT USED TO BELONG TO OLD-TIME SOCCER STAR "DEAD-SHOT" KEEN. IN SOME STRANGE WAY THE BOOTS ENABLED HIM TO PLAY IN DEAD-SHOT'S STYLE. HE WAS SELECTED FOR THE FIRST TEAM OF A LOCAL YOUTH CLUB AND WAS TRAINING FOR A VITAL CUP GAME...

AND SO, THE FOLLOWING MORNING SAW GRAN AND BILLY TRAVELLING IN A TAXI...

WHAT'S AUNT ADA LIKE, GRAN? I CAN'T REALLY REMEMBER HER..!

TAXI

YOU WERE ONLY A BABY WHEN YOU SAW HER LAST! SHE'S VERY RICH... HER AND YOUR UNCLE HERBERT! HE'S GOT A VERY IMPORTANT JOB..!

HERE'S THE HOUSE..!

COR, IT'S LIKE A **PALACE**!

AUNT ADA WAS THERE TO GREET THEM...

MY WORD, HASN'T BILLY GROWN, MARY? HE WAS JUST A LITTLE THING WHEN I LAST SAW HIM... COME IN, BOTH OF YOU!

HOW D'YOU DO, AUNT ADA... NICE TO SEE YOU!

TEN MINUTES LATER...
CAN'T DO ANY HARM PLAYING HERE! I'LL TRY A FEW SHOTS..!
WOMP!

AND A FEW HEADERS..!
BLIP!

BUT THEN...
YOU'RE BILLY, EH? NOT BAD FORM, SON... DO YOU PLAY FOR A TEAM?
OH! YOU-YOU MUST BE UNCLE HERBERT! I-I DIDN'T HEAR YOU COMING!

I PLAY FOR A YOUTH CLUB SIDE THIS YEAR! LAST YEAR I HAD A FEW GAMES FOR ENGLISH SCHOOLS!
DID YOU? MY WORD, THAT'S GOOD STUFF!

I EXPECT YOU'D LIKE TO PLAY PROFESSIONAL FOOTBALL AND TURN OUT FOR ENGLAND ONE DAY, EH? MOST BOYS DREAM OF THAT..!
I'D LIKE TO! BUT I'D HAVE TO BE JOLLY LUCKY...AND WORK HARD!

WHILE YOU'RE DOWN HERE, BILLY, YOU MIGHT LIKE TO CALL IN ON THIS TEAM. THEY'RE AN AMATEUR SIDE AND THEY'RE QUITE GOOD! I'M A DIRECTOR OF THE CLUB...THE ADDRESS IS ON THIS CARD!
GOSH, THANKS, UNCLE!

FERNWAY UNITED! COR, THEY'RE IN THE OLYMPIAN LEAGUE..!
FERNWAY UNITED F.C.
HAMELINE LANE
HERBERT ENFIELD ESQ DIREC

WHERE DID YOU GET THOSE BOOTS, BILLY? THEY'RE A BIT OLD, AREN'T THEY..?
THEY USED TO BELONG TO DEAD-SHOT KEEN...YOU KNOW, THE OLD-TIME PLAYER WHO USED TO PLAY FOR ENGLAND!

THE GREAT DEAD-SHOT KEEN, EH? WELL, YOU'LL GET ON FINE DOWN AT UNITED'S GROUND... HE PLAYED FOR THEM FOR A SEASON OR TWO BEFORE HE TURNED PROFESSIONAL! THEY'VE GOT STACKS OF PHOTOS OF HIM!

THAT EVENING...
FANCY DEAD-SHOT KEEN ONCE PLAYING FOR FERNWAY! I BET THEY'LL BE ABLE TO TELL ME LOTS OF STORIES ABOUT HIM! I DIDN'T WANT TO MISS THE CUP-TIE AT HOME... BUT I'M GLAD I CAME HERE!

AFTER BREAKFAST...
I'M JUST OFF TO FERNWAY UNITED, GRAN! BE BACK FOR LUNCH!
THAT'S THE FOOTBALL TEAM HERBERT'S INTERESTED IN..!
TRUST BILLY TO GET MIXED UP IN FOOTBALL AS SOON AS HE GETS HERE!

AT FERNWAY UNITED'S GROUND, BILLY PRESENTED UNCLE HERBERT'S CARD...
BILLY DANE, EH?.. SENT BY MR.ENFIELD? OKAY... YOU CAN TRAIN WITH US IF YOU LIKE... GO AND GET CHANGED!
GOSH, THANK YOU, SIR!

BILLY SOON MADE FRIENDS WITH THE PLAYERS...
BOP!
WE'RE A SMALL CLUB, BILLY—WITH ONLY FIFTEEN PLAYERS ON THE STAFF! WE'RE NOT DOING TOO WELL AT THE MOMENT... NOT WON A GAME THIS SEASON!

IF WE DON'T WIN SOON... WE'LL FIND OURSELVES RELEGATED AT THE END OF THE SEASON! THAT'LL BE THE *FIRST* TIME SINCE DEAD-SHOT KEEN HELPED THE CLUB GAIN PROMOTION TO THIS DIVISION!

WHAT DID DEAD-SHOT KEEN DO?
IT WAS WAY BACK... YEARS AGO! BUT FERNWAY DIDN'T HAVE A HOPE OF GETTING OUT OF THE SECOND DIVISION UNTIL DEAD-SHOT ARRIVED..!

BILLY COULD IMAGINE THE EVENTS THAT HAD TAKEN PLACE SO MANY YEARS BEFORE...
DEAD-SHOT REALLY SET FERNWAY ALIGHT THAT YEAR! HE WAS THE BEST STRIKER THE SIDE EVER HAD..!

DEAD-SHOT CAME TO US BY CHANCE, INTRODUCED BY A DIRECTOR... JUST LIKE YOU, BILLY! HE SCORED FIFTEEN GOALS IN SIX GAMES..!
HE SCORED THREE IN THE LAST GAME OF THE SEASON... AND FERNWAY WON PROMOTION ON GOAL AVERAGE!

WHEN THE TRAINING SESSION BEGAN...
HEY, TAKE IT EASY THERE! YOU'RE NOT PLAYING IN A MATCH, YOU KNOW!
OUCHHH!

THE TACKLE HAD BEEN AN UNLUCKY ONE...
WELL, YOU WON'T BE PLAYING SATURDAY, TOMMY... THAT'S A BAD ANKLE STRAIN YOU'VE GOT THERE!
OH, NO! THAT'S FIVE INJURED PLAYERS NOW... WE CAN'T EVEN PUT OUT A FULL TEAM! THIS WOULD HAVE TO HAPPEN!

HEY, BILLY... HOW ABOUT YOU? COULD YOU TURN OUT FOR US SATURDAY? JUST FOR ONE GAME... I COULD GET YOU SPECIALLY REGISTERED! RECKON YOU'RE GOOD ENOUGH?
GOSH, I-I'D LIKE TO TRY, SIR... I'D DO MY BEST!

BILLY RACED HOME TO TELL HIS UNCLE...
SATURDAY, EH? WELL, YOU'VE CHOSEN A HARD MATCH, BILLY! FERNWAY ARE PLAYING SLEDHURST TOWN... AND THEY'RE LEAGUE LEADERS! IF YOU CAN HELP FERNWAY WIN THAT ONE... THEY MAY REALLY GET GOING!

IT SEEMED LIKE AGES UNTIL SATURDAY... BUT, THE GREAT DAY ARRIVED AT LAST. AND, AT THREE O'CLOCK...
HURRRRAHHH!
HERE COME FERNWAY!
THAT MUST BE THEIR NEW PLAYER! CRIKEY, HE'S JUST A SCHOOLKID!

THE GAME STARTED, AND ALMOST IMMEDIATELY...
IT'S THE BOOTS! THEY MADE ME SWERVE LIKE THAT WHEN I REALLY WANTED TO PASS...!
COR, LOOK AT THAT LAD GO!

BILLY SLID HIS FINAL PASS ACCURATELY INTO THE PATH OF THE FERNWAY CENTRE-FORWARD...
GOOAAAL!

FOLLOWING THE QUICK GOAL, FERNWAY BEGAN TO PLAY WITH MORE AND MORE CONFIDENCE...
LOOK AT YOUNG DANE... HE NEVER GIVES UP!
HE'S A PROPER LITTLE TERRIER!
THERE'S NO CHANCE OF GETTING THE BALL... BUT THE BOOTS ARE MAKING ME RUN..!

AND THEN THE HARASSED FULL-BACK MADE AN ERROR...
IT'S THERE! OWN GOAL! BUT THAT KID WORKED FOR IT!
WHAT DID YOU DO THAT FOR?
SORRY!

HALF-TIME CAME AND WENT AND STILL FERNWAY WERE LEADING TWO GOALS TO NIL...
GIVE IT TO DANE!
LET THE YOUNGSTER HAVE IT... HE'LL SHOW YOU THE WAY!
FERNWAY! FERNWAY!

AND THEN...
CENTRE IT!
I-I CAN'T SEEM TO STOP... IT'S THE BOOTS MAKING ME GO AGAIN!

THE BALL WAS SWITCHED TO THE LEFT-WING AND BILLY ARRIVED AT JUST THE RIGHT PLACE... AT JUST THE RIGHT TIME...
GOOOAALL!
IT'S BILLY DANE... HE'S DONE IT! THREE UP TO FERNWAY!
BOP!
WHOOOOOOSHH

AND, AT THE END...
FANCY WHACKING THE LEAGUE LEADERS THREE-NIL!
THAT LAD DID IT! Y'KNOW... HE REMINDED ME OF DEAD-SHOT KEEN YEARS AGO! WHAT A SMASHING LITTLE PLAYER!
WELL DONE, BILLY! GREAT GAME, SON!

ON SUNDAY, BILLY AND GRAN RETURNED HOME...
FERNWAY SAID THEY'LL GIVE YOU A GAME ANYTIME YOU COME BACK, BILLY!
THANKS, UNCLE! 'BYE..!
'BYE, ADA... KEEP IN TOUCH!

THERE WAS GOOD NEWS FOR BILLY AT HOME, TOO...
WE DREW THE CUP-TIE, BILLY... WE'VE GOT TO REPLAY ON TUESDAY..!
AND YOU'LL BE BACK IN THE TEAM, THEN..!

BUT, BEST OF ALL, WAS THE PRESENT THAT ARRIVED FROM FERNWAY UNITED...
A PHOTO OF DEAD-SHOT KEEN... WITH HIS AUTOGRAPH ON IT! COR, THAT'S REALLY GREAT!
THE END.

Roy Race's SOCCER

1. Bryan Robson is one of my favourite players. But do you know which club the England captain was with before signing for Manchester United?

2. What is the nickname of Sheffield Wednesday? I'll give you a clue – think of a bird.

3. Which countries do these famous footballers play for: (a) Karl-Heinz Rummenigge (b) Diego Maradona and (c) Paolo Rossi?

4. The player on the right helped England to win the World Cup in 1966. More recently he has found success as manager of Portsmouth. Who is he?

5. If Peter Shilton stopped a shot from Kerry Dixon, which two clubs would be playing?

QUIZ

6. Steve Archibald (left) has made a big name for himself in Barcelona. Before that he helped Spurs to success. Which Scottish clubs did Steve previously play for?

7. Poor Norwich won the 1985 Milk Cup Final, but were still relegated. So were the team they beat at Wembley. Who were they?

8. Two wingers called Barnes have thrilled First Division fans over the past year. One plays for Watford and the other for Manchester United. What are their first names . . . and which Barnes plays for which club?

9. Which of the Home countries does Peter Nicholas play for?

10. Ray Wilkins and Mark Hateley (top) starred for one of the Milan clubs in Italy last season. Was it Inter or AC?

11. Can you tell me the Second Division club in South West London whose name is also associated with the tennis championships held each summer?

12. He was a winger with Manchester United and England. His career was finished by a knee injury. He went on to manage Crystal Palace. Who am I talking about?

13. If I was watching a game at The Dell, who would be the home team?

14. Scotland qualified for the 1986 World Cup Finals by beating which country in a two-leg play-off?

15. Pictured below, one of the most powerful strikers in England is called . . . Regis. How do you spell his first name?

CONTINUED OVERLEAF

Roy Race's SOCCER QUIZ *continued*

16. Complete the full names of these clubs: (a) Stoke (b) Charlton and (c) Brighton.

17. Who was the manager of England during the 1982 World Cup Finals?

18. Which two clubs in Division One have artificial pitches?

19. Former England goalkeeper Tony Waiters led which country to the 1986 World Cup Finals? I'll give you a clue – it begins with the letter 'C'.

20. Which famous Scottish club was the first British team to win the European Cup back in 1967?

21. Who was the manager of Liverpool immediately before Kenny Dalglish?

22. Who are The Dons of Scotland?

23. Can you tell me the name of the Danish international star (right) who has become such a firm favourite with Manchester United supporters?

24. What is the name of West Brom's ground? Is it (a) Highbury (b) The Hawthorns or (c) The Shay?

25. If you saw the Tigers playing the Lions you wouldn't be at the zoo! Which two clubs would you be watching?

26. By what name are Glasgow derbies (below) between Celtic and Rangers commonly known?

27. True or false – both Northern Ireland and the Republic of Ireland wear green shirts.

28. What is wrong with this statement: Everton midfielder Peter Read was chosen as the Players' Player of the Year in 1985.

29. Only two of these three countries have won the World Cup three times – which is the odd one out . . . France, Italy, Brazil?

30. Athlete Steve Cram (below) is a big football fan. But which of the big North-East clubs does he support? Is it Newcastle or Sunderland?

31. Complete the names of these famous Scotland managers . . . (a) —— MacLeod (b) Tommy —— and (c) —— Ormond?

32. What is the full name of Saint . . . Jimmy Greaves's partner on television?

33. Can you sort out this mixed-up footballer . . . RUTELH SITSETLB?

34. In 1967, Wembley staged its first-ever all-London F.A. Cup Final between Spurs and Chelsea. Who won?

35. Who were Britain's lone representatives in the 1978 World Cup Finals in Argentina?

36. He was an elegant midfielder with West Ham, his only club. He was an England international. His nickname was Hadleigh. Now he's a BBC radio commentator. Who is he?

37. In 1953 England lost an international to a foreign team at Wembley for the first time. Who were the victors – Hungary, Rumania or Bulgaria?

38. Name the famous star who found fame with Liverpool and England . . . but who retired after helping Newcastle to promotion. His initials are K.K.

39. Tell me the Rangers and Scotland winger whose name rhymes with 'super'.

40. Is it Vic or Viv Anderson (below) of Arsenal and England?

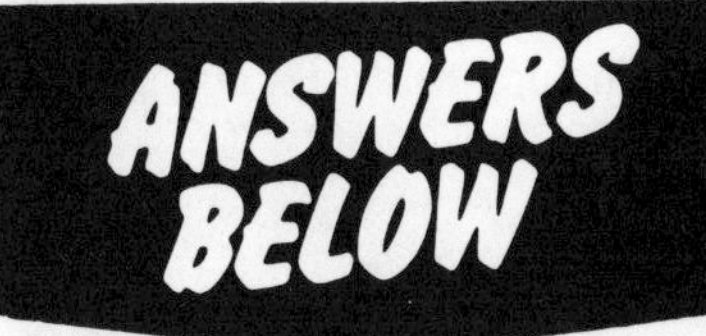

1. West Brom. 2. The Owls. 3. Rummenigge – West Germany; Maradona – Argentina; Rossi – Italy. 4. Alan Ball. 5. Southampton v Chelsea. 6. Aberdeen. 7. Sunderland. 8. John Barnes of Watford and Peter Barnes of Manchester United. 9. Wales. 10. AC Milan. 11. Wimbledon. 12. Steve Coppell. 13. Southampton. 14. Australia. 15. Cyrille. 16. Stoke CITY; Charlton ATHLETIC; Brighton AND HOVE ALBION. 17. Ron Greenwood. 18. Queen's Park Rangers and Luton. 19. Canada. 20. Celtic. 21. Joe Fagan. 22. Aberdeen. 23. Jesper Olsen. 24. The Hawthorns. 25. Hull v Millwall. 26. Old Firm clashes. 27. True. 28. His name is spelt Reid, not Read. 29. France. 30. Sunderland. 31. ALLY MacLeod; Tommy DOCHERTY; WILLIE Ormond. 32. Ian St. John. 33. Luther Blissett. 34. Spurs 2-1. 35. Scotland. 36. Trevor Brooking. 37. Hungary. 38. Kevin Keegan. 39. Davie Cooper. 40. Viv.

Speedie service!

Brought up in England, but as passionate as any Scot who has ever worn the famous dark blue jersey. The Glenrothes-born striker has at times been TOO passionate . . . his temper has got him into trouble with referees. But the Chelsea star is one of the fastest forwards around, living up to his name and his goal record makes David Speedie a respected opponent.

DAN WAYNE BECAME MANAGER OF WOLVERDON F.C. WHEN WOLVES WERE IN DEEP TROUBLE! TO PAY THE CLUB'S DEBTS, ALL THE STAR PLAYERS WERE SOLD AND DAN HAD TO FIELD A TEAM OF INEXPERIENCED YOUNGSTERS. ALTHOUGH THE TEAM TRIED HARD, THERE WAS ALWAYS THE THREAT OF RELEGATION...

WOLVES LOSE AGAIN!

FIVE GAMES WITH-OUT A WIN AT MARLEY ROAD!

WOLVES' KEEPER, PETER BRIGHT, MAKES GALLANT ATTEMPT TO SAVE HIS TEAM!

WE ALWAYS LOSE BY THE **ODD** GOAL! LIKE TODAY... TWO-ONE!

IT'S JUST BAD LUCK!

NO, IT'S NOT! WE'RE NOT **GOOD** ENOUGH... THAT'S WHY!

DAN WAYNE PAUSED OUTSIDE TO LISTEN...

DRESSI ROOM

I CAN'T BLAME THEM FOR FEELING DOWN! THEY NEED SOMETHING TO GIVE THEM A **BOOST**... LIFT THEIR SPIRITS!

DAN TOOK HIS PROBLEM TO THE CHAIRMAN...

IF THE LADS COULD GET A **CHANGE** FOR A FEW DAYS, SIR, IT WOULD DO THEM THE WORLD OF GOOD! A SHORT HOLIDAY MAYBE...?

I WISH I COULD HELP, DAN... BUT THERE'S NO MONEY IN THE KITTY!

DURING THE WEEK...

YOU CAN'T FAULT THE LADS, BOSS... THEY PUT EVERYTHING INTO THEIR TRAINING!

IF ONLY THERE WAS SOME WAY OF RAISING MONEY **OURSELVES**, FRANK! JUST FOR A THREE-DAY HOLIDAY...

OUCHHHH! I'LL **GET** YOU FOR THAT, BARTON! ARE YOU PRACTISING PUTTING THE **BOOT** IN?

IT WAS A FAIR TACKLE, SPUD!

THE PRESSURE OF LOSING IS GETTING TO THEM!

IF YOU WANT THE BALL, SON... HAVE IT!
I'LL WHACK YOU ONE!
LEAVE IT OUT, LADS! WE'RE IN ENOUGH TROUBLE WITHOUT YOU TWO FIGHTING!

AT HOME THAT EVENING . . .
THEY'RE ONLY YOUNGSTERS... THEY DON'T WANT TO STAY IN A POSH PLACE. THEY JUST NEED SOMEWHERE TO RELAX...

JEREMY JOHNSON! WHY DIDN'T I THINK OF HIM BEFORE? HE'LL HELP! HE'S A GREAT WOLVES' FAN...

SURE, DAN... BE MY GUESTS! BUT YOU'LL HAVE TO LOOK AFTER YOURSELVES. THERE'S ONLY AN OLD CARETAKER THERE NOW. THE PLACE IS CLOSED FOR THE WINTER...
DON'T WORRY ABOUT THAT, JEREMY... WE'LL MANAGE! AND THANKS!

ANOTHER CALL ON THE CHAIRMAN...
I DON'T WANT ANY MONEY FROM THE CLUB, SIR, BUT I'D BE GRATEFUL IF I COULD BORROW SOME TRANSPORT!
THE COACH WE TRAVEL IN FOR AWAY MATCHES? SURE YOU CAN, DAN... BUT YOU'LL HAVE TO BUY YOUR OWN PETROL, OKAY?

THE PLAYERS WERE DELIGHTED...
UNITED F.C.
A FREE HOLIDAY? GREAT!
WHERE ARE WE GOING?
IT'S A MYSTERY TOUR! ROUND THE GAS-WORKS AND BACK! HAW, HAW!

THREE HOURS LATER...
A HOLIDAY CAMP! WE'RE NOT STAYING HERE, ARE WE?
IT'S CLOSED!
JOHNSON'S HOLIDAY CAMP
IT'LL SOON BE OPEN... ESPECIALLY FOR US!

WAYNE'S WOLVES, MISTER! WE'RE STAYING HERE UNTIL FRIDAY!
THE BOSS PHONED THROUGH AND TOLD ME! I'LL DO WHAT I CAN FOR YOU. MY NAME'S ALF!

CHOOSE YOUR OWN CHALETS! GO WHERE YOU WANT. ALL THE CAMP ENTERTAINMENT WILL BE OPEN TOMORROW... AND IT'S FREE!
HURRRAHHHHH!

YOU CAN USE ANYTHING YOU LIKE... AFTER YOU'VE SPENT THE MORNING TRAINING!
BOOOOOOOOOOO!

THE FIRST MORNING...
GOOD PLACE TO TRAIN FOR A GOALIE, BOSS. I CAN DIVE ABOUT ON THE SAND WITHOUT PICKING UP A MASS OF BRUISES!
A SMASHING DAY!
IT'S COLD... BUT NICE!

THE WOLVES 'KEEPER SHOWED GOOD FORM, TOO!
GOOD SAVE, PETER!
OH, VERY CLEVER... NOW YOU CAN GO AND GET IT!
I CAN'T SWIM! YOU'LL HAVE TO GO!
THEY'VE FORGOTTEN THEIR WORRIES ALREADY... THAT'S THE MAIN THING!

THEN...
URRGHH! YOU MESSY DEVIL!
GOT IT OFF YOU, THOUGH, DIDN'T I?
A FEW DAYS AGO THAT WOULD HAVE STARTED A PUNCH-UP!

AND CARETAKER ALF GOT THE ENTERTAINMENTS GOING...
GOOD SHOT, MISTER STEELE! YOU CAN THROW AS WELL AS YOU SHOOT GOALS!
MAKE HIM STOP, ALF, OR YOU WON'T HAVE ANY COCONUTS LEFT!

LOOK OUT!
WHEEEEEEE!
MOVE! THEY'RE NEARLY ON TOP OF US!
IF WE HAD GONE TO A POSH HOTEL, THEY'D HAVE BEEN BORED STIFF!
ARRRRGHHHH!
LISTEN TO THAT! THE BOSS HAS GOT THE WIND UP!
DON'T SUPPOSE HE'S EVER BEEN ON ONE OF THESE BEFORE!
CLUCK-CLUCK-CLUCK! YOU'RE CHICKEN, BOSS! HAW, HAW!

AND...
THEY'RE EATING WELL, MISTER WAYNE! THIS IS SECOND HELPINGS FOR ALL OF 'EM!
AMAZING THE DIFFERENCE IT'S MADE! THREE DAYS BY THE SEA, PLAYING KIDS' GAMES ... AND THEY'RE FULL OF THEMSELVES!

ON THE COACH GOING BACK...
YOU'VE GOT TO HAND IT TO THE BOSS! IT'S BEEN A SMASHING HOLIDAY!
WE'RE AT HOME TO SOUTHDEN TO-MORROW. WE'VE GOT TO WIN FOR A CHANGE!
WELL, I'VE BOUGHT THE BOSS A **PRESENT** ...FROM ALL OF US!

THIS IS FROM THE LADS, BOSS! SOMETHING FOR YOU TO WEAR AT THE MATCH TOMORROW... TO BRING US LUCK! AND THANKS FOR THE HOLIDAY!
THAT'S NICE OF YOU! THANKS VERY MUCH!

SOUTHDEN WERE **FOURTH** IN THE LEAGUE... WOLVES, **BOTTOM**!
HOW MANY DO YOU RECKON WE'LL BEAT WOLVES BY, FRANK? TWO OR THREE-NIL?
COULD BE FIVE OR SIX IF WE'RE ON FORM!
WE'D PLAY BETTER IF WE HAD MORE OF OUR OWN FANS HERE!

THERE WERE A FEW LOYAL SUPPORTERS...
WOLVES!
WOLVES!
WOLVES!
WAYNES WOLVES ARE WONDERFUL!
STEELE IS MADE OF IRON!
DUKE DANCER IS KING!
THE YOUNGSTERS NEVER LET US DOWN... WIN OR LOSE! THEY ALWAYS CHEER!

MOST OF THE TIME, WOLVES WERE DEFENDING...
SOON BE HALF-TIME! KEEP THEM OUT, WOLVES!
ANYWHERE WILL DO!
LET'S HAVE ONE THEN, SOUTHDEN!

AND THEN... DISASTER!
IT'S THERE! AN OWN GOAL BY BRIAN LAST!
OH, **NO**!
WOLVES HAVE BEEN UNDER PRESSURE THROUGHOUT!

AT HALF-TIME...
YOU HAD A STROKE OF BAD LUCK WITH THAT OWN GOAL, LADS! BUT DON'T WORRY... KEEP PLAYING AS YOU HAVE AND YOU'LL WIN!
IF YOU GET **BAD LUCK**, YOU HAVE TO GET **GOOD LUCK**, TOO! IT ALL EVENS OUT!
DON'T WORRY, BOSS... WE'LL FIGHT ALL THE WAY!

AND WAYNE'S WOLVES DID FIGHT! JUST BEFORE THE END...
RUN, STEELEY... CHASE IT!
GOOD BALL! WALLY'S SET UP A CHANCE HERE!
COLIN STEELE LASHED IT!
YESSSSS! IT'S THERE!
MAGIC!
CRACKING SHOT, COLIN!

AND SO THE GAME ENDED ALL-SQUARE ...
MAGNIFICENT, LADS!
ALL DOWN TO THAT SEA-AIR WE HAD, BOSS!
WE GOT A POINT!
NO-ONE EXPECTED US TO HOLD SOUTHDEN! BUT WE SHOWED 'EM!

HEY! WHAT ABOUT THAT PRESENT WE GAVE YOU, BOSS?
WE ASKED YOU TO WEAR IT AT EVERY MATCH TO BRING US LUCK!

SMASHING HAT, THAT!
IT'S LUCKY!
OKAY, LADS- I'LL WEAR IT...

BUT I'VE CHANGED THE MESSAGE! THE WOLVES WILL BE THE GREATEST ONE DAY, AND THAT'S A PROMISE!
KISS ME KWIK!
WOLVES FOREVER!
The End

GOALKEEPER

A GREEN-CLAD FIGURE FLEW THROUGH THE AIR, PULLING OFF YET ANOTHER MAGNIFICENT SAVE. GOALKEEPER RICK STEWART WAS IN HIS USUAL SPARKLING FORM FOR TYNEFIELD UNITED'S YOUTH TEAM!
OH, NICE ONE, RICK! A GREAT STOP!
LOVELY ANTICIPATION!
NO WONDER WE DON'T OFTEN LOSE WHEN HE'S PLAYING!

ONE SPECTATOR ON THE LINE WAS EQUALLY PLEASED... TOUGH CLUB MANAGER JIMMY ROCKWELL
GOOD TO SEE YOUNG RICK IN FORM, DAVE. I THINK I'M GOING TO NEED HIM FOR THE FIRST TEAM IN MIDWEEK
WHY'S THAT, BOSS? PADDY CANNON INJURED AGAIN?

YES. A THIGH SPRAIN. BUT I'M NOT WORRIED. I'VE DROPPED THE LAD IN THE DEEP END BEFORE. HE WON'T LET US DOWN...

A GRAVELLY VOICE BROKE IN...
HAH! THAT'S WHAT YOU THINK! YOU'VE GOT A SHORT MEMORY, JIM. THE GAME'S AWAY AT SKULLMERE, AIN'T IT? THE GROUND THEY CALL "THE GRAVEYARD"...?
JOE JACKSON!

THE OLD TYNEFIELD MAN HAD BEEN A SOCCER SCOUT ALL HIS LIFE...
IF YOU'RE GOING TO PICK RICK STEWART, JUST REMEMBER WHAT USED TO HAPPEN TO HIS DAD, GORDON STEWART, AT THAT PLACE...

GOOAAL!
"GORDON WAS A GOALKEEPING LEGEND. HE HAD THE SAFEST HANDS IN SOCCER. IT MADE NO DIFFERENCE..."

"SEVEN TIMES THE BIG MAN PLAYED AT SKULLMERE.."
"...AND SEVEN TIMES HE WAS ON THE LOSING SIDE. ALWAYS THREE-NIL."
YES, THE GRAVEYARD WAS GORDON'S UNLUCKY GROUND ALL RIGHT. I WOULDN'T PICK THE BOY IF I WAS YOU, JIM. YOU'LL LOSE THREE-NIL, SURE AS EGGS ARE EGGS!
JIMMY ROCKWELL'S REACTION WAS PREDICTABLE...
SUPERSTITIOUS NONSENSE! IN ANY CASE, GORDON PLAYED FOR TYNEFIELD CITY, NOT UNITED. HE'S DEAD NOW. RICK IS HIS SON...
YOU'RE THE BOSS, JIM. BUT DON'T SAY I DIDN'T WARN YOU
SONY - PHILIPS
ALL THE SAME, IT'LL BE BEST IF RICK DIDN'T FIND OUT ABOUT ALL THIS. HE'S JUST AS SUPERSTITIOUS AS HIS DAD USED TO BE
THERE'S THE WHISTLE! WE'VE WON AGAIN!
TWO-NIL. ANOTHER CLEAN SHEET FOR RICK!
THAT'S FIVE IN A ROW!

NOT DOING ANYTHING ON WEDNESDAY, ARE YOU, RICK? I WANT YOU FOR THE TRIP TO SKULLMERE WITH THE FIRST TEAM
THAT'S GREAT, MISTER ROCKWELL! I'LL BE THERE. THANKS!

RICK LEFT THE GROUND, ELATED...
COR– IT'S NOT OFTEN I GET THE CHANCE TO PLAY SECOND DIVISION FOOTBALL. AWAY AT SKULLMERE, TOO. SMASHING!

THEN...
YOU BE CAREFUL ON THAT BIKE, YOUNG RICK. SOCCER COMES AFORE CYCLING, Y'KNOW
HALLO, THERE, MISTER JACKSON. STILL FINDING ALL THE STARS OF TOMORROW?

DOING MY BEST, SON– DOING MY BEST. AND THAT'S WHAT YOU'LL HAVE TO DO AT SKULLMERE ON WEDNESDAY. YOU DON'T ALWAYS WANT TO LET IN THREE LIKE YOUR DAD, DO YOU?

WHAT DID HE MEAN BY THAT? "DON'T ALWAYS LET IN THREE LIKE YOUR DAD..."?

HELLO, DEAR. DID YOU WIN TODAY?
TWO-NIL, MUM. DEAD EASY. SORRY– CAN'T STOP!

I'LL SOON SOLVE THE MYSTERY. DAD'S SCRAP-BOOK IS BOUND TO HOLD THE ANSWER

STEWART
TYNEFIELD CITY GO DOWN 3-0 AT SKULLMERE!
THIS IS TAKING AN AGE! I'LL HAVE TO FEED ALL THE INFORMATION INTO MY COMPUTER!

AND SO . . .
SKULLMERE 3 TYNEFIELD
SKULLMERE 3 TYNEFIELD
SKULLMERE 3 TYNEFIELD
SKULLMERE 3 TYNEFIELD CITY
SKULLMERE 3 TYNEFIELD CITY 0
SKULLMERE 3 TYNEFIELD CITY 0
SKULLMERE BEAT DAD'S TEAM SEVEN TIMES IN SEVEN VISITS. AND ALWAYS BY THREE GOALS TO NIL!

BUT THE NEXT ANSWER TO COME UP WAS STAGGERING!
THE GOALS WERE ALWAYS SCORED BY THE SAME MAN, AND THEY ALWAYS INCLUDED A PENALTY! UN-BELIEVEABLE!
GOALSCORERS
JOHNSON HAT-TRICK (ONE PENALTY)
SLADE
SLADE
SLADE
WARREN
KELLY
LLOYD

MY NAME'S STEWART, TOO, BUT I PLAY FOR UNITED, NOT CITY. THE SAME THING CAN'T POSSIBLY HAPPEN TO ME. THERE'S NO NEED FOR ME TO WORRY...

WEDNESDAY EVENING SOON CAME . . . AND RICK WAS QUICKLY IN ACTION . . .
WELL DONE, RICK! TAKE YOUR TIME... DON'T LET THEM HASSLE YOU...!

THE YOUNG GOALKEEPER PLAYED WITH INCREASING CONFIDENCE...
OH, THAT WAS A GOOD SAVE!
I THOUGHT IT WAS IN! HE JUST GOT TO IT!
ONLY SIXTEEN YEARS OLD, HE IS, TOO!
SEE? I KNEW WHAT HAPPENED TO GORDON ALL THOSE YEARS AGO WAS AN OLD WIVES' TALE. THE WAY THE BOY'S PLAYING OUT THERE, HE'LL KEEP ANOTHER CLEAN SHEET.
BUT THE NEXT TWO MINUTES BROUGHT A DISASTROUS CHANGE TO TYNEFIELD'S FORTUNES!
IT'S THERE! McCLEAN HAS SCORED!
BEAT THE YOUNGSTER ALL ENDS UP! HE HAD NO CHANCE!
AND ANOTHER ONE! McCLEAN AGAIN!
YOUNG STEWART WAS UNSIGHTED!
SKULLMERE 2
TYNEFIELD 0
AND FINALLY...
HANDBALL, REFEREE! THAT WAS DELIBERATE!
PENALTY! HE WAS WELL INSIDE THE BOX!
RICK'S STOMACH LURCHED...
IT'S TWO-NIL... AND NOW A PENALTY TO BE TAKEN BY McCLEAN. IT'S ALL COMING TRUE. EXACTLY THE SAME AS HAPPENED SEVEN TIMES TO DAD...

YEESSSS! IT'S THERE!
THREE-NIL! A HAT-TRICK TO McCLEAN!
WE'RE WALKING IT!
BUT DURING THE INTERVAL...
NOW–YOU LOT LISTEN TO ME! FOOTBALL'S ALL ABOUT SCORING GOALS! I DON'T CARE HOW MANY YOU'VE CONCEDED... JUST SO LONG AS YOU GET OUT THERE AND STICK MORE IN THE NET AT THE OTHER END!
OKAY, BOSS.
WE'LL DO OUR BEST
THE HALF-TIME LECTURE HAD A REMARKABLE EFFECT...
UNITED ARE ATTACKING LIKE FURY!
THEY'RE DETERMINED TO GET BACK INTO THE GAME. THEY'LL NEVER PULL THREE GOALS BACK, SURELY...
BUT TYNEFIELD DID NOT STOP.. AND THE GOALS FLOWED FREELY!
GOOOAALL!
1-3
2-3
GOOOAALL!
GOOOAALL!
3-3
4-3
GOOOAALL!
AN UNUSUAL STORY, EH, READERS? IT WAS THE ONE AND ONLY TIME I DIDN'T WANT TO FOLLOW IN MY FATHER'S FOOTSTEPS! BUT THAT 4-3 WIN BROKE THE LOSING STEWART STREAK!
SONY
The End

THE ROY RACE ANNUAL TALK-IN

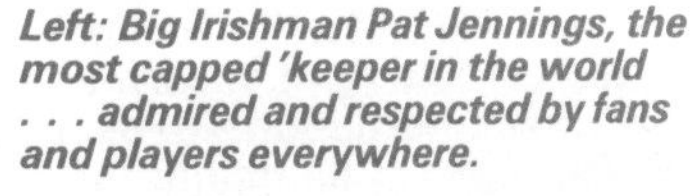

Left: Big Irishman Pat Jennings, the most capped 'keeper in the world . . . admired and respected by fans and players everywhere.

If you want a long career in soccer, be a goalkeeper!

"But, don't you have to be a bit crazy to be a goalie?" you ask. "No, but it helps!" is the answer.

Joking aside, pals, being the last line of defence can often lead to a long stint at the top. Throwing yourself around among flying boots and falling bodies is not everyone's idea of enjoying a job, but it's a proven fact that few goalies suffer serious injuries. Many a custodian has seen a complete change of the other ten men in his team, whilst soldiering on between the sticks.

The most recent example, of course, has been Pat Jennings who, on 13th November, 1985, became the most capped 'keeper in the world. He played for Northern Ireland at Wembley against England, in a vital World Cup qualifying game, notching up number 113! It edged him in front of Italy's Dino Zoff. It was a marvellous milestone for one of the greatest goalies of all time. He was already 40 years old, but had, for a long time, been able to look back on an illustrious career with complete satisfaction.

He'd played for only three major clubs, Watford, Tottenham and Arsenal . . . all with distinction. Pat had started out with the Vicarage Road team in the summer of 1963, but he would have had no idea then that the autumn of his career would not be reached for another 22 years!

The deep-voiced Irishman won his first cap against Wales a year after his Football League debut. It was on 15h April at the Vetch Field, Swansea. It turned out to be a great day for the Irish. They won 3-2.

At the age of 37, he starred for the green-shirted men of Northern Ireland as they reached the World Cup Finals for the first time since 1958. That was in 1982. He was brilliant as his unfancied nation performed heroics and got to the second stages.

Football fans the world over are missing the man they thought would go on and on. Naturally, some day he had to prove them wrong.

At the time this is being written, Pat is back with his old club, Tottenham, keeping himself in shape and making up his mind whether or not to make that long journey to Mexico.

Famous Italian

Whilst those famous big hands were in action in Spain, all eyes were on another world famous goalkeeper . . . Italy's Dino Zoff. He was 40 . . . and captain of his country! He had once kept his nation's goal intact for no less than 1,143 minutes – over ten games – before a forward named Emanuel Sanon, playing for Haiti, whacked the ball past him during the 1974 Finals in West Germany.

Zoff started out with Udinese, making his senior debut in 1961. Two years later, Mantova signed him and in 1967 he joined Naples. On 20th April, 1968, the safest hands in Italy made their International debut versus Bulgaria in a European Championship qualifying game. Dino held his place and helped Italy to win the trophy, keeping a clean sheet in the replayed Final victory against Yugoslavia.

In 1970, the big Italian was a member of Italy's World Cup squad in Mexico, but didn't get a game. Two years later, Juventus paid out a huge sum to secure him. In return, he helped Juve to win several titles and Cups and played in the Champions' Cup Finals of 1973 and 1983.

On the world scene, he represented his country in 1974, as previously mentioned, was first choice 'keeper four years later in Argentina and in 1982 enjoyed his greatest-ever triumph. As skipper, it was he who hoisted the trophy aloft after his nation's tremendous victory over West Germany.

When the World Cup was staged in England during 1966, all eyes were, naturally, on the host nation. But another country caught the eye during the opening group matches. It was Mexico. The reason was their goalie. His name was Antonio Carbajal and it was his fifth Finals . . . a record which is unlikely to be beaten.

He won his first cap in 1948 and had previously been with Mexico to Brazil (1950), Switzerland (1954), Sweden (1958) and Chile (1962). The Mexicans didn't cause any sensations on English soil and the amiable Antonio Carbajal bowed out gracefully from the world scene.

It's ironic to reflect that the next tournament in 1970 was staged in Mexico, but by that time he'd long hung his gloves up!

Getting back to 1966, we can focus on two more custodians. One of them, I'm proud to say, was England's last line of defence. He was Gordon Banks . . . unspectacular, unorthodox, the master of angles

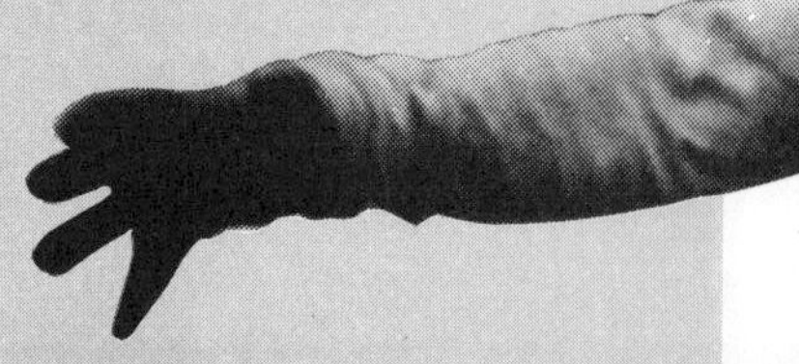

Italian goalkeeping captain Dino Zoff holds aloft the coveted World Cup as his country become the champions of 1982.

and super safe! He's still regarded by many to be the best 'keeper my country has ever had.

He was 28 when he collected his World Cup winners' medal . . . not a great age, but Gordon had his career cruelly cut short. Not long before his 35th birthday, he was involved in a serious car accident, which cost him the sight of an eye. At the time, he was still England's first choice between the sticks. In a matter of seconds, his soccer world had collapsed. Banksie would almost certainly have gone on to add a lot more to his already formidable total of 73 caps.

Whilst England were playing all their matches at Wembley, Russia were performing at venues like Everton, Middlesbrough and Sunderland. They eventually reached the Semi-Finals before losing 2-1 to West Germany. Starring between the sticks for the Ruskies was arguably the greatest goalie to have emerged from behind the "Iron Curtain" . . . Lev Yashin!

Above: the incomparable Gordon Banks, perhaps England's best-ever goalkeeper, and (right) Russia's Lev Yashin of the famous black jersey!

Banks of England

Born in Moscow in 1929, it was his third World Cup, having helped to eliminate England in Sweden during 1958 and going with his nation to Chile for years later. The following year (1963) he played for the Rest of the World versus England at Wembley.

Lev will always be remembered for his incredibly long reach and the fact that he always wore a black jersey!

Going back to the Forties, there stood between the sticks for Manchester City a genial giant of a man . . . Frank Swift. He was born in 1913 and had the latter part of his career disrupted by the Second World War.

When he was only 20, Swiftie made a piece of soccer history. He was in goal for City's F.A. Cup Final triumph over Portsmouth. The year was 1934 and millions will never forget that as the final whistle sounded . . . the youngster fainted!

Big Frank went on to win 19 caps for England and played his last game for the Citizens – his only club – at the end of the 1948/49 season. He was 35 and had been a tremendous servant to the game. He sadly perished in the Munich air disaster.

One year after Frank Swift came into this world, another great goalie was born. His name was Samuel Bartram. His only club was Charlton Athletic and he started playing for them in 1934. It was to be another 22 years before sandy-haired Sam called it a day. He was 42!

Sam has made more League appearances to date than any other player for Charlton . . . 583!

Despite English-born Sam's superb saving

abilities, he never won a full cap for his country. He has been rightly described as the greatest uncapped 'keeper of all time.

Currently in goal for England is a man who created a new 'keeping record on October, 1985. In a World Cup qualifying game against Turkey at Wembley, Peter Shilton won cap number 74 . . . to go one better than Gordon Banks.

Shilts – as he is affectionately called by his team-mates – took a long time to get himself established as England's top custodian. He had to oust Ray Clemence who, at the age of 38, was still doing his stuff between the sticks for Spurs.

Big Frank Swift of Manchester City – a brilliant goalkeeper in the Forties.

Peter Shilton in typical authoratative manner. He is acknowledged as the best in the business.

Sam Bartram, who played for Charlton for 22 years.

Magnificent Shilts

Peter was born in September, 1949, and got his first full call-up in a friendly versus West Germany at Wembley in November, 1970. Gordon Banks was still the number one choice at that time.

During the Seventies, Clemence took over, with Peter getting the occasional look-in, until 1982, when it had become apparent that he was the best in Britain . . . if not the world!

In some way, it was just unfortunate that two goalkeepers of such quality were around at the same time.

Indeed such was the narrow gap between them that former England manager Ron Greenwood played the two in alternate games leading up to the World Cup Finals in Spain before opting for Shilton.

Whilst all the talk has been about top, international-class goalies, spare a thought for an "old hand" in the lower reaches. He's Mike Walker. He'd served Shrewsbury Town, York City and Watford before making his 451st and last League appearance for Colchester United on May 2nd, 1983. He was in his 38th year! He's now coach at the little Layer Road club. Marvellous stuff, Mike!

So, I think I can sum up, in the nicest possible way, by saying that . . . goalkeepers do go on a bit!

Another goalkeeping great – Ray Clemence of Liverpool and Spurs' fame.

GREAT SCOTS!

English clubs have been more successful than any other country's entries in the three European competitions.

Liverpool, Manchester United, Everton, Nottingham Forest, Arsenal, Leeds, Spurs, Manchester City, Newcastle, Chelsea, Ipswich and Aston Villa have all tasted European victory.

West Ham, Birmingham and Wolves have been beaten Finalists.

But any Scot will be quick to tell you that the first British team to win the coveted European Cup was Celtic back in 1967.

And few of the English successes would have been possible without Scottish skills.

It was a Scot, Sir Matt Busby, who led Manchester United to their European Cup conquest in 1968. And while Denis 'The King' Law was injured, Pat Crerand was United's driving force in midfield.

Liverpool won their first European Cup in 1977 without any Scottish players, although the late, great Bill Shankly had paved the way for the Merseysiders to dominate during the 70's.

But in 1978 it was Scotland's Kenny Dalglish who finally pierced FC Bruges' defence. Alan Hansen was as solid as a rock at the back, while Graham Souness was the game's most influential midfielder.

The trio helped Liverpool to beat Real Madrid 1-0 in 1981.

A year later Allan Evans, Ken McNaught and the tigerish Des Bremner were heroes as Aston Villa kept the Cup in England by beating Bayern Munich 1-0.

Brian Clough's Nottingham Forest won the competition in 1979 and 1980. But would they have done it without super Scots Kenny Burns and John Robertson . . . or Frank Gray? Robbo even scored Forest's winner in Madrid against SV Hamburg.

Spurs were the first English team to win the European Cup Winners' Cup in 1963. Two of their stars, goalkeeper Bill Brown and the late John White also wore the dark blue of Scotland with distinction.

Celtic became the first British club to win the European Cup. Steve Chalmers here scores the winner against Inter Milan.

As sharp in the air as they come, Andy Gray leaps high to beat two Everton challengers.

One Scot and one English! Nottingham Forest's John Robertson and Peter Shilton celebrate the 1980 European Cup Final defeat of SV Hamburg.

Since then, Chelsea and Everton have also been Cup Kings of Europe . . . with more than a little help from players such as Charlie Cooke, Andy Gray and Graeme Sharp.

Wherever you look in the English First Division there seems to be a big Scottish influence.

West Ham had a successful 1984/85 – thanks to the goals of Frank McAvennie.

Liverpool are now managed by Scotland's most-capped player Kenny Dalglish. Their captain . . . the stylish Hansen. And Steve Nicol has emerged as one of the most versatile players around for club and country.

Manchester United boast one of the most exciting Scottish talents in Britain . . . little Gordon Strachan.

Wing Wizard

The former Aberdeen midfielder has become a firm favourite with Old Trafford fans, who love his dribbling skills and his never-say-die spirit.

At Chelsea they worship Pat Nevin, whose wing wizardry is always a highlight of the Blues' play. And at the back Joe McLaughlin is one of the most underrated defenders in the game.

Scoring goals regularly is David Speedie, who was born in Scotland but brought up in England. Don't ever mention it in front of the fiery striker that he isn't 100 per cent Scottish, though!

Charlie Nicholas may not have reached the heights he hit with Celtic since his transfer to Arsenal. But the Scot is easily the most popular player at Highbury, where the fans cheer his every move.

Andy Gray and Graeme Sharp spearheaded Everton's double triumph in 1985 when they won the League Championship and Cup Winners' Cup.

Joe McLaughlin of Chelsea, a great Scot who came south of the border to play.

Roy Aitken, another determined performer to wear the blue shirt of Scotland.

Gray returned to Aston Villa during that summer to prove that he is still one of the most feared strikers. And Sharp carried on scoring for Everton.

For many years most of the Scotland team played for English clubs.

But as Aberdeen and Dundee United swung the balance of power in Scottish soccer away from Glasgow to the North East, the national team had a more Tartan look about it.

Dons goalkeeper Jim Leighton has established himself as a player of true international class. Without his string of fine saves during the playoff with Australia in Melbourne. Scotland would not have reached the 1986 World Cup Finals.

Great Players

The back-four has often been an Aberdeen/Dundee United select.

Alex McLeish and Willie Miller are as steady as any central defensive partnership in Britain.

And full-backs Richard Gough and Maurice Malpas have stamped their mark on the national side.

Celtic midfielder Roy Aitken does a great job in midfield, breaking down attacks by winning the ball . . . and starting moves with his shrewd use of the ball.

Team-mate Paul McStay, admired by several English clubs, has both speed and skill which should improve even more as he gets older.

Those who say wingers have no place in the modern game can't have seen Rangers' Davie Cooper. Scottish football has always placed the emphasis on technique and super Cooper is typical of this.

Jim Bett returned from Belgium to join Aberdeen, making an already strong midfield even stronger.

Despite the gloom and doom preached by some critics, football is still the greatest game in the world.

And Scotland provides some of the great players.

Who else but Charlie Nicholas, once of Celtic, now of Arsenal!

Target Men

MARK HUGHES
(Manchester United)

Undoubtedly the best young striker in Britain, it was a huge pity for Hughes that Wales missed out on a place in Mexico. But his chance will come . . . just as the honours, both on a personal level and with United, will keep rolling in.

Target Men

DAVIE COOPER
(Rangers)

A winger of the highest quality, he scored the all-important penalty for Scotland against Wales in Cardiff last year that helped them to Mexico. Was originally with Clydebank, but joined Rangers in a £100,000 deal during 1977. Equally dangerous on either flank.

Target
Men
TONY
WOODCOCK
(Arsenal)
After success with
Nottingham Forest,
Woodcock joined West
German club FC Cologne,
scoring 28 goals in 81
games. Arsenal paid
£500,000 for the striker and
since returning to England,
Woodcock has established
himself as one of Division
One's top stars.
JVC
umbro
Mitre
DELTA

Target Men

KEVIN O'CALLAGHAN
(Portsmouth)

Hit the headlines with Millwall and was transferred to Ipswich. But O'Callaghan never really found his true form at Portman Road and joined Portsmouth in 1984/85 after a loan period. Was outstanding as Pompey pushed for promotion to Division One last season.

Target Men

IMRE VARADI
(West Brom)

Born in London of Hungarian parentage, Varadi started with Sheffield United. Everton paid £80,000 for him but after 26 league games Varadi was on his way to Newcastle. Next stop was Sheffield Wednesday and in 1985 West Brom . . . and a battle against relegation.

Target Men

FRANK McAVENNIE (West Ham)

Few people in England had heard of the St. Mirren ace when John Lyall paid £340,000 for him in the summer of 85. Now, everyone knows the free-scoring McAvennie is a striker of the highest quality. His goals last season made him a hit with the Hammers fans right away.

Target Men

STEVE MORAN
(Southampton)

The former Young Player of the Year hasn't quite come on as many would have hoped. Injuries have affected his progress, but on his day Moran is a striker with the speed and finishing to outwit any defence. Croydon-born and a one-club man.

PETER DAVENPORT
(Nottingham Forest)

His international opportunities have been restricted by the amount of talent available to Bobby Robson. But the Liverpool-born forward has been a consistent goalscorer for Forest, whom he joined as a professional in January, 1982.

Target Men

MO JOHNSTON
(Celtic)

Was snapped up by Watford from Partick Thistle and was an immediate hit in the First Division, averaging a goal every two matches. But Celtic fan Johnston couldn't turn down the chance to join the club he has always loved and went back to Scotland in 1984/85.

Target Men

PETER BEARDSLEY (Newcastle)

After establishing himself with Carlisle, Beardsley 'went West' to join Vancouver Whitecaps in Canada. Had a trial with Manchester United, but Newcastle eventually gave him the chance to prove he could be a top star at home . . . which he has certainly done.

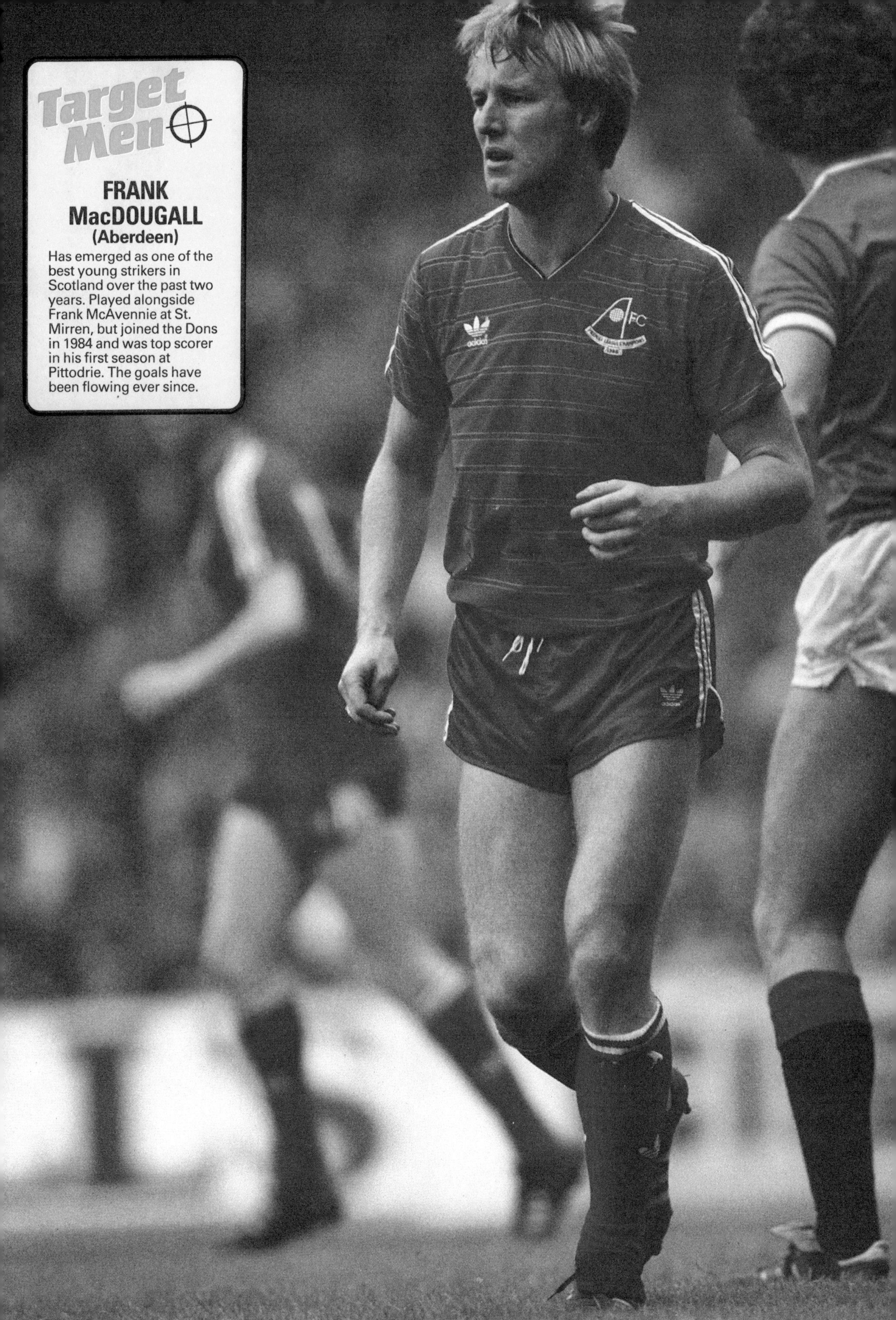

Target Men

FRANK MacDOUGALL (Aberdeen)

Has emerged as one of the best young strikers in Scotland over the past two years. Played alongside Frank McAvennie at St. Mirren, but joined the Dons in 1984 and was top scorer in his first season at Pittodrie. The goals have been flowing ever since.

Target Men

MARK LILLIS
(Manchester City)

Now back in the city where he was born, Lillis shot to fame on the other side of the Pennines with Huddersfield. Billy McNeill brought him to Maine Road to strengthen the side after winning promotion back to the First Division in 1985.

Target Men

JOHN BARNES
(Watford)

Born in Jamaica, but 'made' in England, Barnes is one of the First Division's most talented stars. At home on the wing or at centre-forward, his pace and close control make him a handful even for the best defences. A regular scorer since his debut in 1981.

Target Men

GARY LINEKER
(Everton)

Made his name with Leicester, but now Lineker is a player known all over the world. His transfer to Everton gave him a bigger platform for his considerable skills, while he quickly made a name for himself in the England side with some great goals.

Target Men

CHRIS WADDLE
(Spurs)

Nicknamed Widdly, he cost Spurs £590,000 in 1985 from Newcastle. Has incredible pace and can finish with either foot. Broke into the England team during the 1986 World Cup qualifiers, although it took him a while to reproduce his club form for his country.

Target Men

GARY BANNISTER
(QPR)

Has averaged around a goal every other game for Coventry, Sheffield Wednesday and Rangers. Terry Venables fixed up his £200,000 move just before going to Barcelona. Bannister's speed and skills are ideal for Rangers' artificial surface.

LEE-THAL CHAPMAN!

Lee Chapman was cruelly tagged a £500,000 misfit after his transfer from Stoke to Arsenal. But since moving to Sheffield Wednesday, everything has worked out happy-lee for Chapman! The centre-forward has regained his goal-touch, showing the power that earned him England Under-21 honours. He's one of the most lethal strikers in the business and Arsenal's loss is definitely Wednesday's gain.

THE
HARD MAN

JOHNNY DEXTER, KNOWN AS THE HARD MAN, HAD BEEN RECALLED TO THE ENGLAND SIDE. THE ENGLAND MANAGER HAD MADE IT CLEAR HE WANTED JOHNNY TO DO A PARTICULAR JOB AGAINST A TOP SOUTH AMERICAN TEAM...

REMEMBER, JOHNNY... MARK PELINO AS TIGHT AS YOU CAN. DON'T GIVE HIM ANY SPACE AT ALL. HE'S THE SOUTH AMERICAN DANGER MAN. STIFLE HIM AND WE'LL STAND A CHANCE.
LEAVE IT TO ME, BOSS!

SINCE I MOVED FROM DANEFIELD, I'VE BEEN IGNORED AT INTERNATIONAL LEVEL. THIS IS MY CHANCE TO PROVE THEM WRONG!

JOHNNY WAS SOON IN THE THICK OF THE ACTION...
HE'S OUTJUMPED PELINO!
AS LONG AS THEY KEEP THE BALL IN THE AIR, JOHNNY WILL BE OKAY.

BUT WHEN THE BALL CAME ON THE GROUND...
BRILLIANT! HE'S LEFT THE HARD MAN STANDING!
HE'S TOO FAST FOR YOU, DEXTER!

ONE-NIL!
FANTASTIC! THE SOUTH AMERICANS ARE A DIFFERENT CLASS!
IT'S GOING TO BE A WALK-OVER!
VERY CLEVER! BUT I'M GOING TO MAKE SURE PELINO DOESN'T SHOW OFF AGAIN. FROM NOW ON, HE WON'T EVEN GET THE BALL!
THERE'S A PASS COMING HIS WAY RIGHT NOW... IF I CAN JUST GET BETWEEN HIM AND THE BALL!
GOT IT!
AARGH!
...AND PELINO IS PROTESTING THAT HE WAS FOULED BY JOHNNY DEXTER. BUT THE REF'S NOT IMPRESSED. THE PLAY GOES ON!
EACH TIME THE BALL CAME PELINO'S WAY, JOHNNY WAS THERE...
UUURGH!

THIS TIME, THE SOUTH AMERICAN DECIDED TO DO SOMETHING SPECTACULAR...
GRAAAH!
AND THIS TIME THE REFEREE WAS IMPRESSED...
HE'S GIVEN THE FOUL!
WHAT?
THEN THERE WAS ANOTHER SURPRISE FOR JOHNNY...
YOU'RE BOOKED, DEXTER... YOU'VE BEEN PUSHING YOUR WEIGHT AROUND TOO MUCH IN THIS MATCH!
COME OFF IT, REF... THAT GUY SHOULD GET AN OSCAR FOR HIS ACTING!
THE FREE KICK WAS TAKEN...
WELL CLEARED, HARD MAN!
HE'S LOOKING REALLY DETERMINED!
BUT HE'LL HAVE TO BE CAREFUL. ANY MORE TROUBLE AND HE'LL BE OFF!
A FEW MINUTES LATER...
EERGH!
CAREFUL, DEXTER... THAT WAS ALMOST A FOUL!
BUT IT WASN'T! I'M NOT THAT STUPID!
BY HALF-TIME, THERE HAD BEEN NO FURTHER SCORE...
JOHNNY, YOU DID A GREAT JOB IN THE FIRST HALF... BUT THAT REF IS NO FRIEND OF YOURS. I SHALL HAVE TO MAKE CHANGES...
AW HECK, BOSS... YOU'RE NOT SUBSTITUTING ME?

NO WAY... BUT I AM TAKING YOU AWAY FROM PELINO. IN THE SECOND HALF, YOU'RE GOING TO BE CENTRAL STRIKER!
AND SO...
JOHNNY DEXTER AT CENTRE-FORWARD? I DON'T BELIEVE IT!
PELINO IS GOING TO FEEL LONELY THIS HALF!
THE SOUTH AMERICAN WAS SOON SHOWING HIS SKILLS...
HECK, THIS IS REAL FRUSTRATING, NOT BEING ABLE TO STOP HIM!
PELINO ENDED THE MOVE WITH A FIERCE SHOT AT GOAL...
OOOH! THAT DIPPED AT THE LAST SECOND!
GOOD POSITIONING BY THE 'KEEPER!
YOUR BALL, JOHNNY!
I CAN BE CLEVER AS WELL!
WELL PLAYED HARD MAN... REAL ROY OF THE ROVERS STUFF!

THIS TIME, IT WAS ENGLAND'S TURN TO GO CLOSE TO SCORING...

THE GAME BEGAME A TOUGH MIDFIELD BATTLE...
AT THIS RATE, NO-ONE'S GOING TO SCORE AT ALL, THIS HALF!

WITH TEN MINUTES TO GO, ENGLAND FORCED A CORNER...
TIME'S TICKING AWAY...

THE KICK WAS TAKEN...
JOHNNY'S OUTJUMPED EVERYONE!

THE EQUALISER!
IT'S THERE!

A GREAT GOAL!
GOOD HEADER, HARD MAN... WE'VE GOT A DRAW OUT OF IT!
DRAW NOTHING! WE CAN STILL GET THE WINNER! COME ON!
AND JUST TWO MINUTES LATER...
ALMOST TIME... GOT TO DO THIS MYSELF...
ALL THE FIRST HALF, HE TRY TO TACKLE ME... NOW I TACKLE HIM!
JOHNNY'S GOING LIKE A TANK... BUT PELINO'S AFTER HIM!

HEY, REF... THAT'S A FOUL, IF EVER I SAW ONE!
NNNMPH
BUT THERE WAS NO BOOKING FOR THE SOUTH AMERICAN STAR...
HE GOT AWAY WITH IT!
AND THE REF'S BLOWING FOR FULL TIME. IT'S ALL OVER!
A DRAW!
IF THAT HAD BEEN ME MAKING THAT TACKLE, I'D HAVE BEEN BOOKED FOR SURE!
AFTER THE MATCH...
HEY, ENGLEESHMAN...
HECK... IT'S PELINO! HE'S NOT ON THE TEAM COACH, LIKE THE OTHER GUYS!
AND HE'S DRIVING ON THE WRONG SIDE OF THE ROAD!
YOU SEE THE DIFFERENCE WHEN YOU'RE A STAR, DEXTER... NO-ONE WOULD EVER DARE BOOK ME!
I WOULDN'T BE TOO SURE ABOUT THAT, MATE. TAKE A LOOK...
POLICE
POLICE
EEK!
OKAY, SIR, LET'S HAVE YOUR NAME AND ADDRESS...
HE GOT BOOKED AFTER ALL!
THE END

THE BIG MATCH

a Tommy's Troubles story

The Practice Session

"WHAT'S EVERYONE LOOKING AT? What's going on?" Adam Waller shouldered his way with Cyril Swate through the ranks of Crowhurst schoolboys lining the school rugger pitch. "Speak up, someone. I'm a prefect! I don't ask questions for nothing."

"Shove off, Waller!" shouted someone. "You make the place look untidy!"

Waller glared. "I'll book the lot of you if you don't shut up". He nudged Cyril Swate in the ribs. "Get the notebook out, Swatey. Write down their names when I call them out!"

"Swate can't write!" giggled a voice at the back. "He's mental!"

"That's all you know," fumed Swate. "You'll be the first in the book, whoever you are!"

Gordon Symons, who was in the same class as Waller, poked a finger in Waller's direction. "Swate's not a prefect," he said. "He ain't allowed to write people's names down. Anyway, we're here to watch Tommy Barnes and some of his team practising. That's all!"

Waller blinked, trying to look astonished.

"What are you watching them for? Barnesy and his potty Barnes United team are always practising!" He sniggered. "With all the practice they put in, you'd think they'd be a bit better! My Granny would be more useful on a football pitch!".

"Your Granny's as barmy as you are, Waller!"

There was a roar of laughter and Waller's eyes narrowed nastily.

"If I find out who said that, he'll get a booking for cheeking a prefect!" he said.

On the rugger pitch Tommy Barnes heard the laughter and shouting.

"Waller's shown up," he called to the others. "There's always a blooming row when he goes anywhere."

Ginger Collins had just taken a pass from Skinny Lane and was chesting down the ball, glancing at the rugger goal-posts where Dennis Tracey crouched. Dennis was wearing huge goalkeeping gloves and a peaked base-ball cap, as usual. "Waller ought to be fired off into space on a one-way trip to nowhere," Ginger grunted. "And if you save this shot, Dennis, it'll be the first one you've stopped today!"

Ginger hit the ball sweetly with his left foot and it zipped inside the near post and ran on across the field beyond. Dennis stood in the centre of the goal, hands on hips. "That doesn't count", he objected "I wasn't ready, anyway. I ain't diving all over the place. The ground's too hard!"

At that moment Waller came striding out on to the pitch, waving his arms.

"Get off here, Barnsey. Get off, all of you! This is for rugger ... not that stupid soccer game! Hoppit!"

Tommy, Ginger, Skinny Lane and Dennis Tracey all turned to him. "We know. If we don't get off, you'll book us!" they chorussed. "Well, you can book us all you like and it won't make any difference. We've had permission to practise here. From the Headmaster!"

"So you hoppit, instead!" finished Dennis triumphantly. "Scram!".

Waller quickly altered his attack. He jerked a thumb over his shoulder. "Those kids on the line said you're practising for some match tomorrow. They said you're playing for the TV All-Stars' team. They must be hard up if they asked you to play!"

"That's right, they are hard up," agreed Tommy. "Four of their blokes can't make it tomorrow so we're helping out. They had to ask us," he added modestly, "because we're the only team for miles around who didn't have a game tomorrow!"

"Blooming hard luck on them, then, ain't it!" jeered Waller. "The TV All-Stars are in for a good hiding, with four daft Barnes United idiots in their side. I bet they don't know how rubbishy you are!"

Swate, who had been listening with a frown, said: "Who are the TV All-Stars playing against? A Mother's Meeting team? Haw, haw!"

"Fat lot you know!" sniffed Tommy. "The All-Stars are playing the well-known Sports Celebrities. There are posters up all over the town. On Thornton Eagles' ground, too. Thousands will turn up to watch!"

"It's for Wild Life Charity," explained Ginger.

"Not the sort of wild life you go in for, Waller," added Tommy. "Like bashing people about! It's animal wild-life! Saving poor animals!"

"It's you who need saving!" snorted Waller. "You're stupid!"

The schoolboys on the touchline were getting restive and they began clapping and chanting. "Waller OFF! Waller OFF!"

"Better go," said Swate nervously. "We don't want trouble!"

Waller followed him off the pitch and elbowed through the chanting boys. "Don't say you haven't been warned," he observed darkly. "Tomorrow's game will be a right load of old rubbish with four Barnes United players in the team. They're useless!"

Tommy Barnes and his friends had been invited to play in a big charity match – but Waller and Swate were determined to ruin it!

Waller and Swate took the opportunity to cause more trouble by charging onto the pitch in the charity game and throwing paper rolls in all directions.

The Big Match

THE FOOTBALL CROWD AT Thornton Eagles' ground was over two thousand . . . nearly a record for the club. Tommy and Ginger were enjoying themselves. They had soon realised that the TV All-Stars and the Sports Celebrities were not much better than the teams they played against in their League matches every week.

Goals were what mattered. Goals were what the crowd had come to see. And goals they were getting. Tommy had opened the scoring for the All-Stars. Then Skinny Lane had scored one. Then an actor from a comedy show and a man who ran a quiz programme had each found the net.

For the Sports Celebrities, three goals had been scored by their best player . . . a former player from a league club.

But now the TV All-Stars were back on the attack. A well-known news-presenter booted a loose pass down the middle where it should have been easily cut out by the Celebrities' centre-back. But, as he was a jockey, and very small, the ball dropped over his head and Tommy raced around him. He trapped the ball and looked up. Ginger was racing away to his right.

"Over here!" screamed Ginger excitedly. "I'm clear!"

So am I! thought Tommy. We're both in the clear. Their marking's terrible!

Waller and Swate had reluctantly paid their admission fee and had been shouting all through the first half, jeering at Tommy. Now they stepped up their barracking.

"Get rid of it, Barnsey! You're selfish!" yelled Cyril Swate.

"He's just trying to show off in front of everyone!" screamed Adam Waller. He'd brought several rolls of paper with him and he passed one to Swate. "Let him have it, Swatey. If we don't do something, the TV All-Stars will win and Barnsey will be even bigger-headed than he is already!"

Tommy was on the edge of the penalty area and about to shoot when a roll of paper, unwinding as it flew through the air, wrapped itself around his face and shoulders. His feet tangled and he crashed to the ground.

Everyone laughed. Waller and Swate fell about, holding their sides.

"Did you see that?" Waller kept giggling. "Flat on his face! Stupid twit!"

The Celebrities cleared the ball by mis-kicking it hard and high across the pitch and it bounced over the touchline near Swate, who grabbed it. "Let's hide it. Make 'em all search for it!"

"Better still," said Waller, reaching for the ball, "I'll boot if out of the ground. By the time it's found, everyone will have gone home and Barnsey will get the blame. "We'll say he kicked it!"

Tommy had recovered his feet and he stalked across to Waller with his arms full of paper streamer. "Keep this stuff off the pitch," he protested. "It's blooming dangerous, tripping people up!"

Waller grinned, let the ball drop from his hands and, shielded by Swate, gave it the biggest kick he could summon. Tommy stared in horror and astonishment, watching the ball as it curled high through the air and dropped out of sight over the wall which surrounded the ground.

"BOOOOOO!" The crowd hadn't quite seen what had happened, but they had seen the ball vanish over the wall.

"Tommy Barnes did it!" shrieked Waller and Swate together, dancing about and pointing. "He's a rotten hooligan!"

Ginger came across quickly as Tommy began to march determinedly towards Waller. "Leave him, Tommy. Don't cause trouble! We can get another ball!"

The referee ran over and blew his whistle, gesturing Tommy back on to the pitch, telling him to get on with the game. "I can't get on with the game, ref," Tommy protested. "We haven't got a ball. It's been kicked out the ground!"

The crowd began to chant impatiently. "We want more action! We want more action!"

Waller and Swate took up the cry. "We want more action. Barnsey OFF!"

A football bounced on to the pitch, thrown there by a Thornton Eagles' official. "Play with that one. We'll find the first one later. Just get the game moving again!"

One of the Sports Celebrities seized his chance. He took one look at the TV All-Stars players who were standing in a bunch wondering what all the fuss was about . . . and then booted the ball to the far side of the pitch where a team-mate trapped the pass and started to run. The crowd cheered lustily.

The TV All-Stars' goalie was standing near the centre-circle with his team-mates. The Celebrities player, who was a pole-vaulter and had never played football before in his life, couldn't miss the empty goal. He slammed it into the back of the net and turned with arms raised in triumph.

"YESSSSSS! applauded the crowd. "Best goal of the match!"

Waller and Swate took the opportunity to cause more trouble by charging on to the pitch and throwing the remaining paper rolls into the air in all directions. "Sports Celebrities for Ever! Sports Celebrities for Ever!"

"Get off!" thundered the referee. "You're holding up the game."

Waller and Swate were enjoying it. They chanted and clapped, dancing up and down on the centre-spot. "BARNES UNITED – WHAT A LOAD OF RUBBISH! TOMMY BARNES – USE-LESS!"

"Oh, crumbs!" Swate came to a full stop and grabbed Waller's arm. "Here comes a cop."

"Get those hooligans off!" bellowed the crowd angrily. "We didn't pay our money to see those idiots prancing about!"

"We've done nothing wrong," gulped Waller. "The cops can't touch us!"

"Who says they can't" muttered Swate. "I'm hopping it!" He began to run toward the exit and Waller wasn't far behind.

The game continued. The scores were level now at four-all, until near the end, Tommy picked up a loose ball and, swerving past a leaden-footed defender, took the ball to the bye-line and pushed it back to Ginger who was following up fast. A touch to bring the ball under control and Ginger side-footed it firmly past the advancing 'keeper and into the cover of the net.

"MAGIC!" bellowed the crowd, waving their arms.

It was a great moment for Ginger. He stood with his arms raised. And the goal proved to be the winner.

On Monday morning, the local newspaper carried a big headline: TV ALL-STARS WIN FOOTBALL THRILLER 5–4. HOOLIGANS DISRUPT CHARITY MATCH!

Tommy and Ginger saw the paper on their way to school.

"Hooligans!" said Tommy. "That's Waller and Swate. They ought to cop it. Teach 'em a lesson!"

"They won't, though." Ginger shook his head. "They'll just deny it. They'll say they were at home all that evening . . . that it was two kids

The paper tangled itself all round Tommy and he crashed to the ground.

"Get off, Barnsey!" yelled Waller. "This pitch is for rugger!"

who looked like them."

During morning lessons the headmaster sent for Waller and Swate. He held a copy of the newspaper in his hands as they entered his study and he held it out for them to see.

"Hooligans!" he snorted. "Have you read this yet?"

"No, sir," said Waller innocently. "What's it all about?"

"Whatever it is, it wasn't us, sir," sniffed Swate. "Two other kids who look just like us. We weren't at the footer match!"

"Nor was I," said the headmaster. "I was at home watching television."

"That's right, sir, so was I," nodded Waller brightly. "Good film on, too. All about cowboys and indians in Space or something."

"I didn't watch that rubbish," said the headmaster coldly." I watched the local TV News. It showed scenes from the TV All-Stars and the Sports Celebrities Match!"

Swate felt a cold shiver run up his spine. "D-did it, sir?"

"It did! It showed the trouble caused by two hooligans ... who kicked the ball out of the ground and ran on to the pitch and behaved like lunatics!"

Waller and Swate remained silent ... and sweated.

"I recognised them!" grated the head.

The Result

"TV is a wonderful thing," said Tommy thoughtfully, later in the afternoon.

"It lets you see things as they happen," said Ginger.

"Shut up!" snarled Waller.

"Sorts out the guilty from the innocent," murmured Tommy.

Tommy and Ginger walked to the classroom door and looked back at Waller and Swate who were sitting writing busily at their desks. "Don't leave until you've finished writing your lines."

"You got off lightly," said Ginger. "Kept in every night for a week wasn't too bad. Should cure you of messing up footer matches, though!"

Tommy and Ginger strolled across the empty playground.

"Good, playing for the TV All-Stars, wasn't it' Ginger?" Tommy spread his arms. "All those people watching. And all those stars playing. We were famous for a while."

"So were Waller and Swate!" grinned Ginger. "Recognised by thousands ... including the Headmaster! Ha, ha, ha!"

THE END

The magic of Man United

Everton 0: Manchester United 1. And captain Bryan Robson's expression and medal clutched in hand says it all. The Red Devils are the greatest!

Manchester United are the best supported club in England . . . and the number one draw when they play away.

Their team of international superstars pull in the fans like no other side.

Yet back in 1878, when the club was created, things were very different.

Called Newton Heath, the club was formed by workers from the Lancashire and Yorkshire Railway Company.

And while Old Trafford today is one of the most modern stadiums in the world, Newton Heath played on a mud heap in the middle of a disused clay pit!

The dressing-rooms were in the back of a nearby pub!

In 1902 Newton Heath became Manchester United . . . and a legend was born.

In 1907/8 United won their first League Championship and a year later the F.A. Cup was theirs.

Since then, honours have come United's way regularly. But the man who really put United on the soccer map was Sir Matt Busby – who once played for rivals Manchester City!

An historic picture: members of the ill-fated Man. Utd club who were devastated by the Munich air disaster in 1958.

Centre (just recognisable as the man you see on television) is Bobby Charlton as his header beats the flat-footed Benfica 'keeper for the first goal in United's 1968 European Cup victory.

Who else but the lethal Denis Law? The cheeky, nimble-footed Scot notched many such goals for the famous Manchester club.

Sir Matt, or just plain Matt as he was then known, put together one of the most promising teams ever seen in English football, called the Busby Babes.

They won the League in 1956 and 1957 and looked set to conquer Europe.

But in 1958, returning from a European Cup tie in Belgrade, United's plane crashed on take-off on a snow-covered Munich Airport.

Eight players and three officials died . . . including Duncan Edwards, the young giant who was tipped to become the greatest player of all-time.

Sir Matt lived and ten years later his dream of seeing the European Cup at Old Trafford became reality.

United had household names such as Denis Law, Bobby Charlton and George Best. And at Wembley in 1968, swept on by a wave of emotion, United beat Portuguese aces Benfica 4-1 to become Kings of Europe.

Relegation

When Sir Matt finally stepped down to become a director, United hit a bad spell. They found it difficult to find a man to follow Sir Matt and in 1974 the unthinkable happened . . . the Red Devils were relegated.

But, as everyone knows, under Ron Atkinson, United have risen to the top again, becoming the biggest box office hit in soccer.

Atkinson has never been afraid to spend. A few eyebrows were raised when he signed Bryan Robson for a record £1.7 million from West Brom. But no-one now would doubt the value of the United and England skipper.

Robson led United to successive F.A. Cup triumphs

The commanding figure of Norman Whiteside in the thick of the action, here moving away from Everton's Kevin Ratcliffe. Below left: Paul McGrath.

in 1984 and 1985, the latter won in dramatic style.

United were down to ten men against Everton following the dismissal of Kevin Moran.

But a brilliant goal by Norman Whiteside gave United the Cup.

Whiteside began his career as a striker. But in 1985 Atkinson shrewdly converted the Irish youngster into a midfielder and United observers say Whiteside's presence is now as important to the team as Robson's . . . praise indeed.

United fans have had some great Scottish heroes, such as Law and Willie Morgan.

Little Gordon Strachan is the latest Tartan Terror at Old Trafford, dazzling the supporters with his own brand of magic.

Danish Ace

Jesper Olsen took a while to settle down following his £500,000 transfer from Ajax. But the Danish ace showed his true form and has become a firm favourite with the Stretford End.

Home-produced stars such as Paul McGrath, Graeme Hogg and Arthur Albiston have carried on the Old Trafford tradition of finding their own youngsters.

Manchester United are Magic . . . you can see it on car stickers and scarves up and down the county.

Because United don't just belong to Manchester.

They are more than a club. They're an institution . . . a one-off in a class of their own.

Liverpool, Everton, Arsenal, Spurs – all great clubs.

But, as the Old Trafford fans sing, There's Only One Manchester United.

Super Scot Graeme Sharp cost only £125,000 from Dumbarton in 1980. But he would be worth many times that amount now, having established himself as one of the First Division's most lethal marksmen. His goals helped Everton to win the Championship and European Cup-winners' Cup in 1985 . . . not forgetting the F.A. Cup in 1984. Graeme has won Under-21 and full caps for Scotland, establishing himself in the squad that qualified for Mexico.

SHARP-SHOOTER GRAEME

X Y
CASTLEBURN CITY
BACK ROW IAN CLARK (MANAGER) · PADDY MURPHY · SAILOR WATSON · TONY PRICE · MICKY HUNTER · SANDY BEECH · TAFFY EVANS
FRONT ROW DICK SHARP · HERBIE JENKINS · TREVOR SCOTT (CAPTAIN) · JIMMY CHELSEY · DUSTY MILLER · SERGEANT BUCKET (COACH)

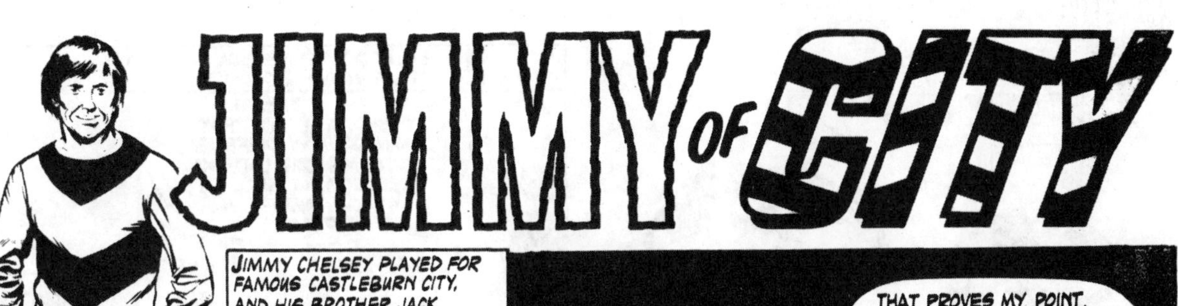
JIMMY OF CITY

JIMMY CHELSEY PLAYED FOR FAMOUS CASTLEBURN CITY, AND HIS BROTHER JACK FOR THEIR LOCAL RIVALS CASTLEBURN UNITED. WHEN CITY AND UNITED DREW IN THE FINAL OF A KNOCKOUT TOURNAMENT, AND THE TWO SIDES HAD TO MEET AGAIN IN A REPLAY, IT CAUSED GREAT EXCITEMENT IN THE CHELSEY FAMILY...
CITY ARE BOUND TO WIN! THEY SHOULD HAVE WON LAST TIME, BUT JACK SCORED THAT EQUALISER IN THE LAST MINUTE!
THAT PROVES MY POINT. UNITED WILL WIN BECAUSE THEY CAN STAY THE COURSE! CITY RAN OUT OF STEAM! A FEW MINUTES LONGER AND THEY'D HAVE BEEN BEATEN!

MEANWHILE, MANAGER ERIC MILLS OF UNITED, AND HIS CAPTAIN PHIL HUGHES WERE WAITING IN A CASTLEBURN HOTEL...
I DON'T GET IT, ERIC. WHY SHOULD CITY'S MANAGER WANT AN UNOFFICIAL MEETING HERE?
I'VE NO IDEA, PHIL. BUT HE PARTICULARLY INSISTED THAT YOU SHOULD COME!

THEN...
HERE'S IAN CLARK NOW!
AND HE'S GOT CITY SKIPPER TREVOR SCOTT WITH HIM!

A MAN WHO WAS ALWAYS BUBBLING OVER WITH IDEAS, IAN CLARK WAS SOON EXPLAINING WHAT HE HAD IN MIND...
I THOUGHT IT WOULD BE A MARVELLOUS GIMMICK IF WE MADE JACK AND JIMMY CAPTAINS, JUST FOR THIS ONE MATCH. TREVOR AGREES... BUT PHIL WOULD HAVE TO CONSENT, TOO! WHAT DO YOU SAY?

MILLS WAS THE CAUTIOUS TYPE, HOWEVER...
HMM... IT NEEDS THINKING ABOUT...
I AGREE WITH TREVOR, ERIC—IT'S A GREAT IDEA!

COME ON, ERIC, OUR MAIN JOB IS TO ENTERTAIN THE FANS— AND THEY'D JUST LOVE THIS!
WELL, ALL RIGHT THEN. THREE OF YOU ARE IN FAVOUR, SO WE'LL DO IT—IF JACK AND JIMMY AGREE!

JACK WAS THE PLACID TYPE. HE TOOK THE NEWS OF HIS TEMPORARY HONOUR CALMLY...
SURE, ERIC, IF THAT'S WHAT YOU WANT. NOT THAT IT CAN MAKE ANY DIFFERENCE TO OUR GAME. OUR LADS KNOW THEIR JOB SO WELL THEY HARDLY NEED A CAPTAIN!

BUT EXCITABLE JIMMY TOOK IT VERY DIFFERENTLY!
ME—CAPTAIN OF CITY? BUT HOW CAN YOU BE SURE I WON'T MAKE A MESS OF IT?
THERE'S NO NEED TO BLOW YOUR TOP, LAD! IT'S ONLY FOR ONE AFTERNOON!

ON THE WAY HOME...
THE LIBRARY! JUST THE PLACE!

I'LL MAKE A SUCCESS OF THIS JOB IF IT KILLS ME!
THE MATHEMATICS OF FOOTBALL

THAT EVENING...
WHERE'S JIMMY THEN? I'VE NEVER KNOWN HIM MISS A WESTERN BEFORE. HE'S MAD ON THEM!

JIMMY WAS UP IN HIS ROOM... SWOTTING!
PHEW! I NEVER KNEW THERE WAS SO MUCH TO LEARN ABOUT FOOTBALL.
SET PIECES

NEXT MORNING, WHEN THE CITY MET FOR TRAINING, JIMMY HAD SOME SURPRISING NEWS FOR SWEEPER SANDY BEECH...
D'YOU REALISE YOUR JOB IN DEFENCE MEANS PROTECTING A TRIPLE ZONE BASED ON THREE ISOSCELES TRIANGLES, SANDY?
GET AWAY? I'M NOT EVEN SURE I KNOW WHAT ONE OF 'EM IS!

BUT WHEN IT CAME TO SHOOTING PRACTICE, JIMMY WAS BADLY BELOW FORM...
THAT'S THREE IN A ROW YOU'VE MISSED, JIM! WHAT'S UP?
I SEEM TO HAVE GOT THE TRAJECTORY WRONG!
IF THAT ARC REPRESENTS THE AREA THE GOALIE CAN COVER IN THE TIME ALLOWED TO POSITION HIMSELF, THE LINE OF THE BALL SHOULD MAKE A TANGENT TO THE CURVE!

AT THE END OF THE TRAINING PERIOD...
I'M WORRIED, IAN. JIMMY IS TAKING THIS CAPTAIN LARK TOO SERIOUSLY. HE'S GONE ALL HIGHBROW ON US.
WELL, IT'S TOO LATE TO CHANGE THINGS NOW! IT WAS OUR IDEA..!
22

CITY AND UNITED FANS PACKED THE STADIUM FOR THE MATCH...
GOOD OLD JIMMY!
GOOD OLD JACK!

THE OPENING MINUTES MADE THE CITY FANS UNEASY...
JIMMY SEEMS A BIT SLOW TODAY. HE SHOULD HAVE HAD THAT BALL!
ABCDE

BUT JIMMY MADE AMENDS BY GAINING POSSESSION FROM A TACKLE.

THEN...
THAT'S NO GOOD! THEY'RE ALL MARKED! HE TOOK TOO LONG IN CROSSING IT!

IT WAS JACK WHO CLEARED THE BALL...
SEE? THE UNITED DEFENCE HAD STACKS OF TIME TO GET INTO POSITION!

JIMMY BEGAN TO SHOUT EXCITEDLY AS THE BALL WENT FOR A THROW-IN.
MICKY, YOU'RE TOO SQUARE— GET BACK A YARD! SANDY, COME UP TO FORM A RIGHT ANGLE...!

IAN CLARK WAS GROWING WORRIED...
JIMMY'S CONFUSING THEM WITH ALL THAT CHAT! WHY DOESN'T HE LEAVE THEM TO GET ON WITH IT?

THE OLDER CHELSEY BROTHER SPOTTED THE OPPORTUNITY FOR A BREAK...

TWO AGAINST TWO! IT'S A CHANCE FOR UNITED!

UNITED'S NORMAN HAMPTON HAD AN EASY TASK TO SLOT HOME JACK'S SHREWDLY-ANGLED PASS!
IT'S A GOAL!
UNITED ARE ONE UP!

PAT TURNED TRIUMPHANTLY ON CLIVE!
WHAT DID I TELL YOU? IT'S UNITED ALL THE WAY!
CITY AREN'T PAYING ATTENTION TO JIMMY'S ORDERS. WHEN THEY DO, IT'LL BE DIFFERENT!

BUT JIMMY'S ADVICE WASN'T PROVING MUCH HELP...
SANDY— REMEMBER YOUR TRIANGLES!

JACK'S THROUGH...!

IT'S THERE! JACK'S MADE IT TWO FOR UNITED!

WHEN HALF-TIME CAME...
I'VE NEVER SEEN CITY PLAY WORSE... THEY'VE GONE TO PIECES!

JACK'S DOING ALL RIGHT, BUT I'M MAKING A PROPER MESS OF THINGS!
THAT'S BECAUSE HE'S CONTENT TO PLAY IT BY EAR! YOU DO THE SAME! FORGOT ALL THAT BOOK-LEARNING STUFF!

BUT THE BOOKS ARE SCIENTIFIC, IAN! THEY'RE WRITTEN BY EXPERTS WHO'VE SPENT A LIFETIME STUDYING THE GAME...

JIMMY, YOU DOPE, YOU DON'T NEED TO LEARN FOOTBALL FROM BOOKS! YOU'RE A BORN PLAYER! DO WHAT COMES NATURALLY, AND IT'LL BE RIGHT, BELIEVE ME!

AS THE GAME RESTARTED, JIMMY MADE UP HIS MIND TO DO BETTER.
JACK'S BETWEEN ME AND THE GOAL... WHAT DOES THE BOOK SAY ABOUT THIS..?

BLOW THE BOOK! THE CHAP WHO WROTE IT HAS NEVER MET MY BROTHER JACK!

JIMMY SKILFULLY SIDESTEPPED HIS BROTHER...
THAT'S MORE LIKE IT, JIM!

BUT JACK RECOVERED AND HUNG ON...
WHEN THOSE TWO GET AT EACH OTHER IT'S CERTAINLY WORTH WATCHING!
JIMMY SCREWED THE BALL TOWARDS GOAL...
HE'S HIT THE BAR!
HARD LUCK, JIMMY!
GOOD TRY!
FOR A MOMENT JACK RELAXED HIS CONCENTRATION... IT WAS ALL JIMMY NEEDED!
IT'S THERE!
THAT MAKES IT 2-1!
CITY ARE BACK WITH A CHANCE!
THE GOAL PUT NEW HEART INTO CITY!
COME ON, CITY, LET'S HAVE THAT EQUALISER!
GOALKEEPER SAM YOUNG THREW HIMSELF FULL-LENGTH, BUT...
THE GOAL'S WIDE OPEN...!
HE'S MISSED IT!

NEXT SECOND...
WHAT A SAVE!
JACK STOPPED A CERTAIN GOAL THERE!
BUT A FAMILIAR FIGURE WAS FOLLOWING UP!
IT'S IN! THEY'RE TWO EACH!
JIMMY'S DONE IT AGAIN!
WHAT ABOUT IT NOW THEN? CITY ARE RIGHT ON TOP!
NOT FOR LONG! THERE'S TIME FOR UNITED TO WEAR THEM DOWN.
BUT CITY AND UNITED WERE STILL BATTLING DESPERATELY WHEN THE WHISTLE BLEW...
IT'S ALL OVER!
OH, NO— IT CAN'T BE!
WHAT HAPPENS NOW, REF? DON'T SAY WE'VE GOT TO START ALL OVER AGAIN?
NO. THE RULES OF THE COMPETITION STATE THAT YOU SHARE THE CUP. SO YOU TWO CAPTAINS HAD BETTER GO UP TOGETHER.
WELL, YOU COULDN'T HAVE A FAIRER RESULT THAN THAT!
GOOD OLD JIMMY!
WELL DONE, BOTH THE CHELSEYS!
GOOD OLD JACK!
THE END

World Cup LEGENDS

THE World Cup is the biggest prize in football . . . the stage for the best players to show their skills.

For one month every four years, millions of fans in every Continent watch the 24 Finalists battle for glory.

But while only one team can win, the World Cup Finals always leave us with the memory of many new stars.

The drama of Mexico, 1986, is still fresh in our minds.

But no-one who saw the previous Finals in Mexico, in 1970, will ever forget the brilliant Brazil team that many critics believe is the greatest side of all-time.

Brazil's hardest game was against England, with Jairzinho scoring the only goal of the game.

But it almost rained goals in the stifling heat of Mexico when the Brazilians turned on their own brand of magic.

There was Rivelino – nicknamed Revelation – who burst upon the international scene. They said he could shell peas with his left foot! He could certainly fool goalkeepers with his incredible swerving free-kicks.

In 1970 Pele, surely the greatest of them all, underlined his stature in world football. But back in 1958 the Brazilian teenager took the world by storm in the Finals in Sweden, scoring a memorable solo goal as his country won the trophy for the first . . . but not the last . . . time.

Geoff Hurst wrote his name in the history books by becoming the first player to score a hat-trick in the World Cup Final.

Yet the West Ham sharpshooter had barely established himself in the England set-up when Sir Alf Ramsey gave Hurst the nod ahead of the free-scoring Jimmy Greaves.

Hurst scored three as England beat West Germany 4–2 after extra-time . . . and become a World Cup legend.

Italy's Paolo Rossi turns jubilantly after scoring against West Germany. They won 3–1.

Above: Geoff Hurst heads for goal in 1966 and (right) Gerry Armstrong of N. Ireland celebrates victory over Spain. The big striker was in great form against the host country.

The overall leading scorer in the World Cup Finals is West Germany's Gerd Muller, who was nicknamed Der Bomber.

Muller scored 10 goals in Mexico and four years later added another four to his tally as the Germans won the competition in front of their own fans.

Needless to say, it was Muller who scored the winning goal in the 2–1 win over Holland . . . his last at international level because the Bayern Munich goal-machine announced his retirement from the national team.

Franz Beckenbauer was Germany's captain that day, the highlight of a career that began with his first appearance in the 1966 tournament in England.

Beckenbauer played in midfield then. But he moved into defence to become one of the most accomplished sweepers of all-time.

Franz, called The Emperor, missed the chance of playing in a fourth successive Finals in 1978 because he was with the New York Cosmos.

But Beckenbauer was back on the World Cup beat in 1986 . . . as his country's manager, of course.

A good showing in the World Cup Finals can not only lead to fame . . . but fortune.

Gerry Armstrong had never quite made the grade in England with Spurs and Watford, where he was known as The Judge . . . because he sat on the bench so often!

But in Spain, 1982, Armstrong hit the headlines in a big way. His never-say-die style typified the Irish spirit and he scored the goal that gave Ireland a shock 1–0 win over the host nation.

After the Finals, Armstrong signed a lucrative contract with Spanish club Real Mallorca and went on to further his reputation in the soccer-mad country.

Zbigniew Boniek may not be easy to say. But Italian giants Juventus paid a small fortune for the signature of the Polish midfielder after he led his country to third place in Spain.

And many of the Honduran stars who did so well in 1982 were able to leave the poverty of the Central American republic to boost their bank accounts with Spanish clubs.

One of the fairy-tale stories from Spain was Paolo Rossi.

The Italy striker had only just returned to big-time soccer following a ban after a bribes scandal, although he still fiercely denies any part in it.

Italy started the tournament slowly, looking anything like potential World Champions.

But against all odds, Italy stunned Brazil by winning 3–2, with Rossi scoring an unforgettable hat-trick.

Rossi topped the World Cup goal chart with six, the

Jairzinho of Brazil in action – and it's a goal! He was just one of a superb South American team.

last coming in Italy's 3–1 win over West Germany. What a way to come back after two years in the wilderness.

Eusebio, the fabulous Portugal striker, played in just one Final, in 1966. But he scored nine goals, most of them blockbusters from outside the penalty area.

Surely no player has ever struck the ball harder than the Black Panther? Even from 40 yards the opposing goalkeeper could find his hands stinging . . . if he managed to get in the way of the ball, that is!

Of course, the World Cup always throws up unlikely heroes.

Zbigniew Boniek of Poland.

Back in 1950, Larry Gaetjens scored the goal that gave the USA a 1–0 win over England . . . and soccer hadn't even taken off in the States then.

It was some consolation to Alf Ramsey, England's right-back that day, that he went on to lead England to World Cup victory 16 years later, becoming a Sir in the process.

In 1966 the diddymen from North Korea arrived in England and stunned Italy by winning 1–0. The goal was scored by Pak Doo Ik . . . a name that still causes red faces in Italy.

Proving it was no fluke, the Koreans went 3–0 up against Portugal, before Eusebio decided enough was enough and inspired Portugal to a 5–3 win with some memorable long-range goals.

Scotland left Argentina stung by a defeat by Peru and an embarrassing draw with Iran. And it even needed an own-goal by an Iranian player to prevent the Scots from complete humiliation.

The standard of football in the Third World is now first-class and not even the super-powers underestimate the 'unknowns' from Central America, Africa or Asia.

Italy were losing 1–0 to Cameroon in 1982 before a late goal earned them a point. They were minutes from going out of the competition they eventually won . . . and only an unfortunate slip by the Africans' goalie Thomas N'Kono allowed Graziani to score.

Algeria were responsible for probably the biggest World Cup shock of all in Spain. They beat mighty West Germany 2–1 and failed to qualify for the next round only on goal-difference.

Honduras drew with Spain and Northern Ireland in Spain and lost 1–0 to Yugoslavia only after a debatable penalty. Had the Central Americans won they, not Spain, would have met England in the Quarter-Finals.

The real thrill of Cup football is seeing David beat the soccer Goliaths.

Everyone loves a superstar . . . but the magic of the World Cup is also the shock result – as long as your country isn't on the receiving end!

HOT-SHOT HAMISH
with MIGHTY MOUSE
Featuring HAMISH BALFOUR and KEVIN MOUSE

HOT-SHOT HAMISH AND KEVIN 'MIGHTY' MOUSE PLAYED FOR PRINCES PARK F.C. IN THE SCOTTISH PREMIER DIVISION. KEVIN WORKED IN ST. DUNCAN'S HOSPITAL AND HE, HAMISH AND WEE WALLY CAMPBELL AGREED TO GO TO THE NEW YEAR FANCY DRESS PARTY...
WHAT SORT OF FANCY DRESS WILL YE WEAR, LADS?
WELL, WE HAD A BRIGHT IDEA...
...AND THOUGHT WE'D COME AS FAMOUS FOOTBALLERS!
WE BOUGHT WIGS AND THINGS...

I'M MARK HATELEY!
I'M KENNY DALGLISH!
AND I'M IAN RUSH!

THOSE THREE ARE ALL GREAT GOAL-SCORERS!
WHAT DO YE HAVE TO DO TO SCORE GOALS? WHAT'S THE BEST WAY?
OCH! THAT'S EASY, MON! YE HAVE TO BE ACCURATE!

IF YOU SHOOT TOO NEAR TO THE GOALIE... HE'LL SAVE IT!
HURRAHHH!

AND IF YE SHOOT TOO FAR FROM THE GOALIE... YE MISS THE GOAL, TOO!
BOOOOO!

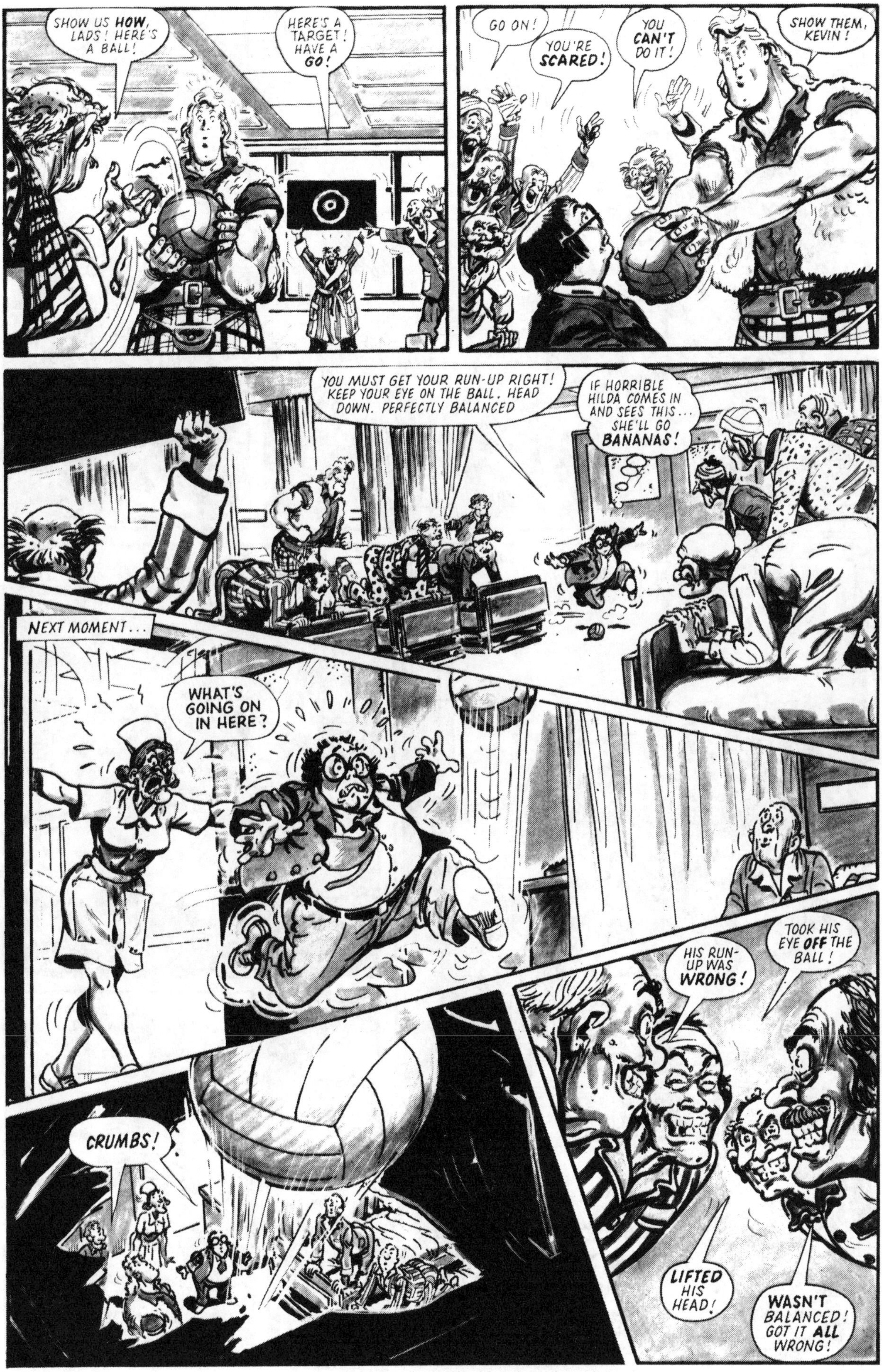

YOU MUST GET YOUR RUN-UP RIGHT! KEEP YOUR EYE ON THE BALL. HEAD DOWN. PERFECTLY BALANCED

IF HORRIBLE HILDA COMES IN AND SEES THIS... SHE'LL GO **BANANAS**!

NEXT MOMENT...

WHAT'S GOING ON IN HERE?

CRUMBS!

HIS RUN-UP WAS **WRONG**!

TOOK HIS EYE **OFF** THE BALL!

LIFTED HIS HEAD!

WASN'T BALANCED! GOT IT **ALL** WRONG!

IT'S NO USE YOU SNEAKING OFF, YOU COWARDY CUSTARD! YOU'RE GOING TO BE IN HOT WATER OVER THIS! I'LL SEE TO THAT!
SHE'S GOT EYES IN THE BACK OF HER NUT!
YOU'RE IN HOT WATER! AND HERE IT COMES! I'M TRYING TO HAVE A BATH UP HERE!
URRRGHHH!
HILDA'S CATCHING IT!
AND NEXT TIME... I WON'T LET YOU HAVE YOUR BALL BACK!
GNNURRR!
I KNOW YOU LOT! YOU'RE FOOTBALLERS! IF EVER I SEE FOOTBALLERS IN MY HOSPITAL AGAIN... I'LL SORT YOU OUT!
THAT'S THE END OF OUR FANCY DRESS OUTFITS!
WE'LL HAVE TO THINK OF SOMETHING ELSE!
NO WAY I'M GOING BACK IN THERE DRESSED AS A FOOT-BALLER!
BEFORE THE FANCY DRESS PARTY, PRINCES PARK HAD A MATCH...
LET'S START THE NEW YEAR RIGHT, EH, LADS? WITH A WIN! IF YE GET A RESULT TODAY, I'LL TAKE YE ON A SUMMER TOUR TO HAWAII!
LOSE... AND YE'LL DO DOUBLE-TRAINING EVERY DAY IN NINETEEN-EIGHTY-SEVEN! GOT IT?

SO DO I...
WE'D BETTER WIN. I FANCY HAWAII!
YOUR ORDER, SIR. PINEAPPLE PUDDING AND A COCONUT SANDWICH!
IT WASN'T AN EASY GAME. CLOGGEM UNITED WERE TOUGH!
HOPPIT, FATTY!
EEEEK! ELBOWS! I'LL GET HIM FOR THAT!
PETER PAN
HAMISH GOT HIS SHARE, TOO!
PERFECTLY FAIR. PLAY ON!
AHHHH!
THAT REF WOULDN'T GIVE A FOUL IF THEY CAME ON THE PITCH ARMED WITH MACHINE-GUNS!
JUST BEFORE HALF-TIME...
YEESSSSS! ONE UP TO CLOGGEM!
DIRTY GAME!
CLOGGEM ALWAYS PLAY DIRTY... IT'S THE ONLY WAY THEY KNOW!
MISTER McWHACKER WASN'T AMUSED!
IT WON'T BE DOUBLE-TRAINING FOR YOU LOT IN THE NEW YEAR! IT'LL BE TRIPLE-TRAINING! YOU WON'T HAVE A SPARE MINUTE TO YOURSELVES!
THERE GOES OUR HAWAII HOLIDAY!
NOT YET!
THE SECOND HALF IS TO COME!

BOOOOO!
RUBBISH!
I WAS ONLY TRYING TO BE ACCURATE!
I'M GOING TO BELT IT AT THE GOALIE AND HOPE FOR THE BEST! I DINNA WANT TO LOSE THAT HAWAII TRIP!
WEE WALLY WORKED HARD ON THE WING...
BOOOOOO! ANOTHER FOUL!
OCH, DINNA SAY ANYTHING, OR THE REF'LL BLOW UP! THAT'S A GOOD CENTRE!
HAMISH MET THE BALL ON THE VOLLEY!
IT'S THERE! THE EQUALISER!
THE GOALIE'S CHICKEN! HE DUCKED!
DON'T BLAME HIM!
NEAR THE END, KEVIN HAD A CHANCE ...
MOUSE! MOUSE! MIGHTY MOUSE!
CAN'T GET PAST THAT LOT... MIGHT AS WELL HAVE A GO!
CAN'T ALWAYS BE ACCURATE!! BUT THEY ALL COUNT!
YESSSSS! AN OWN GOAL!
HALF A DOZEN OWN GOALS THERE!
JUST AS YOU WANTED!
WE STARTED THE NEW YEAR WITH A WIN, BOSS!
AND SO, PRINCES PARK WON... TWO-ONE!
DO WE GO TO HAWAII?
YESSSSSSSS!

THAT EVENING, AT ST. DUNCAN'S . . .

LADIES AND GENTLEMEN!.. FROM PRINCES PARK FOOTBALL CLUB... HAMISH BALFOUR, WEE WALLY CAMPBELL AND MIGHTY MOUSE!

IF THEY TRY TO GET IN HERE DRESSED AS **FOOTBALLERS**, THEY'LL GO OUT ON THEIR EARS! I WON'T STAND FOR IT!

DRESSED AS . . .

SCHIAFFINO

TARZAN . . .

. . . AND THE APES!

CAPI

MAYBE it's because they're Londoners . . . that's why they're capital stars!

Not quite the right words of the famous cockney song. And, of course, many of the top stars were not born in London.

But the capital performers thrill Londoners with their super skills.

London football fans are spoilt for choice, in many ways.

While other major cities, such as Liverpool, Manchester and Sheffield have only two top teams, London boasts FIVE sides in Division One and FIVE in the Second Division.

Their very own Top Ten!

And just 'up the road' are Watford and Luton, giving London fans more options than football followers anywhere else in the country.

The North v South rivalry has been going as long as football.

VIV ANDERSON (Arsenal) and GLENN HODDLE (Spurs).

TONY COTTEE (West Ham United).

KERRY DIXON (Chelsea).

And in recent years, it must be said, it's the North that's come out on top honours-wise.

But don't dare mention Southern Softies anywhere in London!

Is there a tougher tackler anywhere in the League than Spurs' iron man Graham Roberts? He tackles like a tiger and his challenges bite like Jaws.

And when it comes to exciting the fans, is there anyone better than Glenn Hoddle?

The Spurs midfielder finally established himself in the England team last season, gaining the confidence that an extended run in the side gives.

Hoddle added steel to his skills, making him a truly all-round star.

Over at Arsenal, Highbury fans usually watch a team of internationals . . . players who have won international fame at one level or another.

If Charlie Nicholas is the favourite of the North Bank, local hero Stewart Robson could be the player to really make a name for himself in the game.

The powerhouse midfield star is from the same mould as his more famous namesake Bryan. A player who can win the ball . . . and start an attack with a pin-point pass.

At the back, full-backs Viv Anderson and Kenny Sansom are just about the most dependable in the League.

Steady in defence, they are always ready to lend weight to the attack. No wonder both are permanent fixtures in the England squad.

There can be no argument about one of London's

sharpest sharpshooters . . . it has to be Chelsea's Kerry Dixon.

The England striker has kept up an average of a goal every other game during his career with Reading and Chelsea . . . not forgetting his international goals.

Dixon topped the First Division goal chart in 1984/85, his debut season in Division One. And those who doubted his ability have long since eaten their words.

Deadly Dixon forms one of the most feared partnerships in the League with David Speedie. And the man who must take much credit for the goals of Dixon and Speedie is winger Pat Nevin.

At his best he is unstoppable . . . and he's at his best very often!

His jinky runs down the flanks have the Bridge faithfuls cheering and his stream of centres give the Chelsea strike-force goalscoring opportunities galore.

Another prolific strike-force can be found in East London, where West Ham's Frank McAvennie and Tony Cottee have quickly made a big name for themselves.

Supermac hit the headlines by scoring against Australia on his Scotland debut. What a pity so many of his West Ham goals became victim of the television ban.

Cottee is a real tiny terror, a pocket dynamo. Small in stature but big on talent, defenders go potty when Cottee is around . . . because a goal usually isn't far away.

QPR fans will tell you they have the most inspirational captain in the First Division in Terry Fenwick.

He was a left-back with Crystal Palace. But Terry Venables converted 'Fen' into a central defender and it is in this position that he's established himself for club and country.

He never stops urging his team on, and is also a free-kick and penalty specialist.

So is Millwall's Steve Lovell, Mr. Reliable from the spot. His goals have forced him into the Welsh squad and helped the Lions to promotion from Division Three.

Crystal Palace and Charlton – 'brothers' at Selhurst Park – did well last season. Mike Flanagan showed he still has plenty of goals left in him, while Palace unearthed a new goal star in Phil Barber, who delights in popping the cross in from all angles.

Wimbledon's style may have earned them criticism. But there is no denying the Dons place the emphasis on attack, with Stewart Evans and Alan Cork popping in the goals regularly.

Fulham have become famous for selling players. But they still manage to produce new stars and last season Paul Parker emerged as one of the Second Division's outstanding young players.

There are many more stars who light up London . . . making them real Capital gains!

TERRY FENWICK (Queens Park Rangers).

McStay must stay!

FORMER Young Player of the Year Paul McStay is on the wanted list of many top English clubs. But the Celtic and Scotland midfielder is one of the most popular players at Celtic Park and manager David Hay is keen to keep the attacking midfielder who has a big future.

And since making his full Scotland international debut in a 2-0 win against Uruguay at Hampden Park on September 21st, 1983, Paul has established himself as a player of world class ability.

Cannonball CRAIG

YER BUBBLE-AND-SQUEAK IS ALL READY! BUT I'VE COOKED IT LIKE HOME-MADE *FUDGE*, THIS TIME! CUT UP INTO LITTLE CUBES...!
GOSH!

YOU CAN TAKE IT TO SCHOOL IN THIS BAG, SEE... EAT A LUMP JUST BEFORE THE GAME, AND THEN SOME MORE AT HALF-TIME!
I'LL BE ABLE TO MAKE SURE THE EFFECT OF THE **BUBBLE-AND-SQUEAK** LASTS RIGHT THROUGH THE *WHOLE GAME!* SMASHING!

ARMED WITH HIS 'SWEETS', CANNONBALL CRAIG SET OFF...
WISH ME LUCK!
SLAM A COUPLE IN FOR ME, CRAIG!
MIND YOU DON'T NEGLECT YOUR LESSONS, LAD...!

BUT THAT DAY, CRAIG COULDN'T THINK OF *ANYTHING* EXCEPT THE VITAL GAME!
THONK!
WAKE UP, CARTWRIGHT! STOP DREAMING ABOUT *FOOTBALL*, AND **CONCENTRATE ON YOUR WORK!** I'VE GOT MY *EYE* ON YOU, LAD!
OUCH! S-SORRY, MR. PERRY...!

CRAIG TRIED HARD. BUT AS THE TIME TICKED AWAY...
ONLY TEN MINUTES TO THE END OF THE LAST PERIOD... *IT'S TIME I TOOK ONE OF MY* **BUBBLE-AND-SQUEAK SWEETS!**

BUT EVEN AS HE DIPPED HIS HAND INTO THE BAG...
AH-HAH! *SECRET SWEET-SCOFFER*, EH? I **WARNED** YOU, CARTWRIGHT...!
OO-ER!

BAG OF PRECIOUS 'SWEETS' WAS SNATCHED AWAY!
THESE CAN JOIN THE REST OF THE RUBBISH THAT I'VE HAD TO CONFISCATE FROM THIS CLASS!
OH, NO! P-PLEASE, SIR! YOU... YOU CAN'T...!

THEY'RE NOT JUST ORDINARY SWEETS! I..I NEED THEM FOR THE MATCH! IT... IT'S VITAL, SIR...
WHAT ARE YOU RAVING ABOUT, BOY..?
BLAAM!

HOW DARE YOU MAKE FUN OF ME? SWEETS BEFORE FOOTBALL, INDEED! IT'S ONLY BECAUSE THIS GAME IS SO IMPORTANT TO THE SCHOOL THAT I'M NOT GIVING YOU AN HOUR'S DETENTION!

CHEER UP, CRAIG! MAYBE OLD PERRY WILL GIVE 'EM BACK AFTER YOU'VE SCORED A HAT-TRICK AGAINST RIDGETOP!
WHAT'S SO IMPORTANT ABOUT A BAG OF OLD SWEETS, ANYWAY?
IF ONLY YOU KNEW! MY STARS, WHAT A MESS...!

AS CRAIG CHANGED FOR THE VITAL GAME...
I'LL HAVE TO NIP BACK TO SCHOOL AT HALF-TIME, AFTER PERRY'S GONE, AND GET THE SWEETS OUT OF HIS DESK! IT'S MY ONLY CHANCE! I...I'LL BE USELESS WITHOUT THEM...!

UNAWARE OF CRAIG'S PLIGHT, HUNDREDS OF SLEETHORP BOYS, AND SEVERAL MASTERS, SAW THE TEAMS KICK-OFF...
THAT'S IT... GET THE BALL TO CARTWRIGHT!
HAVE A GO, CANNONBALL! SHOW US THAT SUPER-SHOT..!
OH, LOVELY PASS!

BUT...
COR! HE'S PASSED IT TO THE OTHER SIDE!
WHAT'S THE MATTER WITH HIM! WHY DIDN'T YOU SHOOT, CARTWRIGHT?
WHAT'S THE USE? WITHOUT MY BUBBLE-AND-SQUEAK, I COULDN'T EVEN REACH THE GOAL FROM HERE, LET ALONE SCORE!

MEANWHILE, BACK IN CRAIG'S CLASSROOM...
NO-ONE LOOKING! HEH, HEH! NOW TO FIND OUT WHY CARTWRIGHT GOT IN SUCH A PANIC OVER THESE SWEETS! THEY MUST BE RATHER SPECIAL..!
CHOCOLATE

POPPING A CUBE OF BUBBLE-AND-SQUEAK INTO HIS MOUTH, MR. PERRY BEGAN TO CHEW IN EAGER ANTICIPATION!
I..UUM!... LOVE CONFISCATING SWEETS! BUT THEN I CAN'T.. SLURP!.. HELP IT IF I'VE GOT A.. MUNCH!.. SWEET TOOTH, CAN I? MMMM!

STILL CHEWING THOUGHTFULLY, MR. PERRY MARCHED OUT TO THE BICYCLE SHED...
CAN'T THINK WHY CARTWRIGHT IS SO FOND OF THESE, THOUGH! FUNNY SORT OF TASTE! SEEMS TO GO... RIGHT DOWN INTO MY... LEGS..!

NOW IT'S... SPREADING THROUGH MY WHOLE BODY! A SORT OF... TINGLING! BY JOVE, I...I DO FEEL SPRIGHTLY THIS EVENING..!

PERRY'S BODY BEGAN TO VIBRATE WITH THE ...STERIOUS ENERGY OF THE BUBBLE-AND-SQUEAK!
SQUEEK!
CLANK!
MY LEGS... DON'T SEEM TO BELONG TO ME! GOING FASTER, AND F-FASTER! OO-ER! WHAT'S HAPPENING? THIS IS RIDICULOUS..!

YEEEOWWWW!
VWOOOM!

OUT INTO THE BUSY STREET PEDALLED THE SUPER-CHARGED MR. PERRY!
I... CAN'T STOP! WALLLLP! OUT OF THE WAY..!
WHIZZZ!
...P.C. TWENTY-NINE TO ALL CARS! STOP AND DETAIN SHORT FAT CYCLIST, BREAKING SPEED-LIMIT THROUGH BUILT-UP AREA! ESTIMATED SPEED OVER FORTY MILES AN HOUR!

A... CYCLIST? S-STONE ME... WHAT AM I SAYING?

BY NOW, MR. PERRY HAD WHIZZED RIGHT ROUND THE BLOCK!
OH, NNNNNO!
HE'S HEADING STRAIGHT FOR THAT BUS!
HE'S DONE FOR! I C-CAN'T LOOK..!

SOMEHOW, MR. PERRY SWERVED AT THE LAST SPLIT-SECOND!
BWAAK!
CRUUNCH!
S-STONE ME!
HE'S SMASHED CLEAN THROUGH THAT FENCE!

AS IT HAPPENED, THE SLEETHORP PLAYING-FIELDS LAY JUST BEYOND...
WHOOOOAAAAAHHH!
L-LOOK OUT... IT'S OLD PERRY!
GOOD GRIEF!
WHAT'S HE TRYING TO DO... BREAK THE LAND-SPEED RECORD?

CRAIG GUESSED AT ONCE WHAT HAD HAPPENED!
THE GREEDY PERISHER MUST HAVE BEEN SCOFFING MY BUBBLE-AND-SQUEAK SWEETS!
STOP ME... P-PLEASE! DO SOMETHING! AAAAHHHH!

GNNNNNF!
THWOMP!
HE'S STOPPED, ALL RIGHT! GOOOAAAAL!
HE'S THERE! GOOD OLD PERRY!

BUT CRAIG CARTWRIGHT WASN'T INTERESTED IN THE PLIGHT OF MR. PERRY...
PERRY, ARE YOU ALL RIGHT? WHAT'S HAPPENED, MY DEAR FELLOW..?
UNNNNNHHH!
THERE'S MY SWEETS! THEY'VE FALLEN OUT OF PERRY'S POCKET!

IN THE EXCITEMENT, NO-ONE SAW CRAIG SNATCH UP HIS PRECIOUS SWEETS...
OLD PERRY'S STILL CYCLING... WITHOUT A BIKE!
A FORM OF NERVOUS TWITCH, BY THE LOOK OF IT! POOR CHAP MUST HAVE BEEN OVER-WORKING!
GET HIM BACK TO THE PAVILION FOR FIRST-AID!

RIGHT, YOU BOYS... FIX UP THE NET, SO'S WE CAN GET ON WITH THE GAME!
I'VE JUST GOT TIME TO EAT A B-AND-S CUBE! BY THE TIME THE GAME RESTARTS, THE EFFECT OF IT SHOULD BE WORKING AT FULL BLAST!

MOMENTS LATER, THE GAME RE-STARTED, WITH RIDGETOP SCHOOL STILL LEADING 1-0...
NOW THEN, CARTWRIGHT, LET'S SEE WHAT YOU CAN DO WITH THAT PASS!
HE'S A LONG WAY OUT! THE WAY HE'S BEEN PLAYING, HE HASN'T A HOPE OF SCORING...!

BUT NOW THE AMAZING ENERGY OF HIS GRANDPA'S BUBBLE-AND-SQUEAK WAS COURSING THROUGH CRAIG CARTWRIGHT'S LEGS!
HE.. HE'S DONE IT! CRAIG'S EQUALISED! GOOOOAAAAAL!
FIZZZZZ!
BWAAMPF!
OH, MY STARS, WHAT A SHOT!

I TOLD YOU TO WATCH OUT FOR CARTWRIGHT'S SUPER-SHOT!
HE TOOK US BY SURPRISE! BUT DON'T WORRY! HE WON'T GET ANOTHER CHANCE!

AS THE GAME WENT INTO THE SECOND-HALF...
UUUNNNF!
CRAIG CAN'T EVEN GET NEAR THE BALL!
IT'S NO WONDER... WITH FOUR OF THE RIDGETOP KIDS MARKING HIM!

THEN, AS THE LAST MOMENTS WERE TICKING AWAY...
IT'S GOING TO CRAIG AGAIN! CAN HE GET THE WINNER?
NOT A CHANCE! THOSE RIDGETOP KIDS WILL BE ON HIM, BEFORE HE CAN EVEN TRAP THE BALL!
WHO SAID ANYTHING ABOUT TRAPPING IT..?